Snack Time

Establishing healthy eating for life
through Snack Time in the early years.

By
Jenni Clarke

'There is a growing emphasis in the UK on the contribution of diet to health status and health outcomes. Childhood nutrition contributes to immediate health, and may set dietary patterns for later life.'
Effectiveness of Interventions to Promote Healthy Eating in Pre-school Children Aged 1-5 years; Health Education Authority 1998

Snack Time

ISBN 1 905019 19 X

© Jenni Clarke 2005
Cover photograph © Sarah Featherstone

Cover design by Kerry Ingham

First published in the UK, October 2005
The Key Issues series is edited by Sally Featherstone

'Key Issues' is a trade mark of Featherstone Education Ltd

Published in the United Kingdom by
Featherstone Education Ltd
44 - 46 High Street
Husbands Bosworth
Leicestershire
LE17 6LP

Printed in the UK on paper produced in the European Union from managed, sustainable forests

Contents

Introduction

Health and nutrition have become key issues in our lives, with the increase in diet related illnesses and obesity. The aim of this book is to highlight how important the early years are for developing a healthy lifestyle. The ideas contained in Snack Time will equip people caring for and educating young children with a range of ideas for promoting awareness of healthy eating and the experience of healthy eating as part of daily life.

Our children's health is paramount to a healthy society in the future. It is so easy in the very busy lives we all live to use quick, convenient foods that we know children will eat, but this option is not doing our children any long term favours.

Promoting healthy eating is an issue for people at different levels, parents, carers and teachers, health practitioners, the government and the children themselves.

'There is a growing emphasis in the UK on the contribution of diet to health status and health outcomes. Childhood nutrition contributes to immediate health, and may set dietary patterns for later life.'
Effectiveness of Interventions to Promote Healthy Eating in Pre-school Children Aged 1-5 years; Health Education Authority 1998

In March 2004 the Schools Minister, Stephen Twigg said,

'Figures show that one in seven fifteen year olds and one in six twelve year olds are obese. We must put this right, and headteachers have our backing 100 per cent when it comes to helping our children eat healthily. A healthy body is a healthy mind.'
www.croner.co.uk 2004

In September 2004 the Government unveiled a Healthy Living Blueprint for schools:

> All schools will be supported to do more to encourage children to eat sensibly, stay physically active and maintain good levels of personal health. Schools will be encouraged to use a range of resources to give children the knowledge, skills and understanding they need to lead healthy lives, not just through what is taught, but also the school's organisation and 'whole-school' environment.

The health secretary also published a survey which found that young people who regularly eat fruit at school as part of the School Fruit Scheme consume more fruit outside school hours.

Schools have been teaching the healthy eating message for years, there are many elements of healthy eating in the QCA science guidance for different key stages, but as Lucy Ward, education correspondent for the Guardian, reported in July 2004:

> 'Pupils may be learning about healthy eating in the classroom but they still choose chips in the school canteen.'
> The Guardian Newspaper; July 13 2004

Learning about healthy eating is not enough; children need to experience it. Many schools are looking at the school meal issues and only have healthy options for the children, but this only denies certain foods during the school day, and we all know how something denied can appear much more attractive when it does appear.

Healthy foods need to be a familiar part of a child's everyday life. Experience of healthy eating at a young age is essential, much research shows that eating patterns developed in early childhood tend to be continued into adulthood. The earlier children are introduced to fruit and vegetables, the more they will enjoy them and the more frequently they will eat them.

Eating healthily is based on knowledge of what constitutes a balanced diet; and becoming used to eating a varied and balanced diet is very important during the first few years of life. In its report 'Nutrition and Pre-School Children' the British Nutritional Foundation lists ten key facts about nutrition and pre-school children:

1. In the last fifty years pre-school children's diets have changed dramatically and 'the inclusion of fruits and vegetables is crucial in terms of eating a mixed diet later in life.'

2. The majority of pre-school children are receiving a range of nutrients essential for healthy growth, however studies revealed that vitamin A, zinc, copper and iron were not being eaten in sufficient amounts.

3. Parents and carers can promote healthy eating and physical exercise in children by ensuring that they set a good example.

4. 'Obesity is now considered to be a global epidemic.' Obesity in young children is likely to continue into adulthood, and the prevalence for obesity in our 3-4 year olds almost doubled between 1989 and 1998.

5. Both diet and physical exercise need to be influenced as early as possible, and it is the responsibility of all sectors in society.

6. Children can learn to eat well and exercise through observation and experience.

7. The government has a responsibility to ensure that everyone can afford a healthy diet.

8. There are Surestart schemes across the country which aim to promote the best start in life, but there needs to be more partnership between agencies to achieve sustainability and community needs.

9. 'The Good Food Project in Burnley, aims to help children to learn how to love good food. Through food-related activities, such as gardening, cooking, shopping and budgeting, it aims to raise awareness of healthier food and its relationship with the environment.'

10. Teddies Nurseries developed a nutritional policy, they highlighted the need for good overall balance rather than 'good food' and 'bad food'. The policy included training the staff and keeping parents informed of new research etc.

On the BNF website you can find leaflets and advice sheets on healthy living, one of which is: 'The Balance of Good Health, putting advice into practice.'

The Government's Balance of Good Health (illustrated above) is a model of how to eat healthily and is based on the 8 guidelines for a healthy diet (see box below). It shows the types and proportions of different foods that should be eaten over a period of time. The Balance of Good Health applies to all healthy individuals over five years of age, and can be gradually applied for pre-school children, but does not apply to individuals with special dietary requirements. If you, or any child you work with, is under medical supervision you should check with your doctor to see whether you should use this guide.

8 guidelines for a healthy diet

- Enjoy your food
- Eat a variety of different foods
- Eat the right amount to be a healthy weight
- Eat plenty of foods rich in starch and fibre
- Eat plenty of fruit and vegetables
- Don't eat too many foods that contain a lot of fat
- Don't have sugary foods and drinks too often
- If you drink alcohol, drink sensibly

You should choose a variety of foods from each of these four food groups every day:

- **Bread, other cereals and potatoes**
- **Fruit and vegetables**
- **Milk and dairy foods**
- **Meat, fish and alternatives**

Foods in the fifth group, i.e. foods containing fat and foods containing sugar, can be eaten sparingly as part of a healthy balanced diet, but should not be eaten instead of foods from the other food groups, or too often or in large amounts. Having a variety of foods in the diet is important for health - it is not necessary to follow the model at every meal, but rather over a day or two.

Eating fruit and vegetables is known to be a great contributor to a healthier lifestyle. They are a good alternative to crisps and sweets as a between meals snack. Fruit and vegetables are also important for future life, as they can help to prevent obesity, heart disease, diabetes, strokes and cancer. The World Health Organisation recommends that we eat five portions of fruit and vegetables every day.

The National School Fruit Scheme

Many schools have used the Government offer of free daily fruit to reinforce teaching about healthy eating through science, numeracy and literacy.

Many of the schools have also found that children settle to their tasks better, have increased attention and are generally better behaved since embarking on the scheme. This is not really surprising as young bodies are using energy for growing as well as learning, and a low energy level will result in lethargy and irritability.

The health secretary published a survey in Autumn 2004 that found young people who regularly eat fruit at school consume more fruit outside school hours.

'Nutrition and Pre-School Children' British Nutritional Foundation 2003. This report can be found on the following website www.nutrition.org.uk

According to www.thesnackpack.net the initial evaluation of the National School Fruit Scheme has shown that it is popular with children, teachers and parents.

'There is some evidence that the scheme is encouraging children to choose fruit in preference to less healthy choices. In some instances children are reported to have overcome their initial reluctance to eat fruit or to try new fruits, largely as a result of positive peer pressure.'
www.thesnackpack.net. 2002

Good nutrition is essential during early childhood. Young children require high levels of energy because they are growing so quickly and becoming more active. This is also a vital time for healthy tooth development and prevention of decay. They need foods high in energy and rich in nutrients, as well as a good supply of protein, calcium, iron and vitamins. This diet should be presented and eaten as part of small and frequent meals

Parents and practitioners also have a responsibility to offer a wide range of different sorts of foods, so children can become used to different flavours, textures and smells. When children have had experience of a wide range of healthy foods in their youth, they can make informed choices when they are older.

Although children's eating habits are shaped through a variety of routes, educational settings offer a unique opportunity for facilitating and encouraging healthy eating alongside the development of academic and social skills. Practitioners can provide opportunities for young children to experience different foods in a relaxed and social situation, where new experiences are part of the everyday environment.

'Young people's eating patterns can be shaped through a variety of routes. Schools offer a most important opportunity for educating children on nutritional issues and facilitating and encouraging healthy eating patterns alongside the development of academic and social skills.'
www.thesnackpack.net. 2002

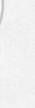

Using this book

This book is for anyone who works with young children:
* parents
* child minders
* breakfast clubs
* after school clubs
* pre schools
* nurseries
* schools.

Snack Time will equip you with a range of activities and ideas for promoting healthy eating that can be used and adapted to the children you work with.

You will find a range of ideas of how to use snack time as a valuable learning experience, not just to cover curriculum objectives but also to introduce a variety of healthy food into the children's day. The aim is for children to experiment, explore and investigate different food.

For each snack food you will find a range of activities to suit different age groups. You can choose the ones suitable for the children in your setting/classroom:

0-3 year old children need to experience the different foods prepared in different ways as well as helping with simple cooking activities, encourage them to use all their senses as appropriate

3-5 year old children will be able to do more of the preparation, cooking and investigation; they will enjoy growing their own food and role-playing.

5-7 year old children will be able to make more accurate predictions, in depth investigations and recordings of findings.

The snacks can be presented as:
* a daily snack time, with a general structure and use of the suggested 'snack time' rules,
* a café type set up in an area in the setting prepared with a menu card for the day, where children can self serve drinks and snacks or be served by another child or an adult. It would be useful to have an adult in this area when the café is open to enhance the learning opportunities
* a daily maths or science focus time for small groups of children
* art of a science, literacy or maths lesson - as a stimulus, problem solving element or investigation.

The Linked ideas and activities can be used as:
- 🖋 Activities in independent learning areas,
- 🖋 Activities for groups to access during a focus time,
- 🖋 Part of 'golden time'
- 🖋 Activities linked to a wider topic or project

The snack ideas are intended to be incorporated in your weekly planning, but many can last much longer, it is up to the children and the adults to explore and investigate as much as is needed.
It is good practice to re-visit the snack types, so that children can:
- 🖋 try something that they were not ready to the last time
- 🖋 realise how their taste preferences have changed over time
- 🖋 reinforce the discoveries and knowledge surrounding a particular food.

We have included a range of activities with similar foods, so that each time you revisit a food type you can have a different emphasis.

There are many books and resources that can enhance the children's play and understanding and you may decide to ask parents and others in the community for information, books, posters etc. on the different foods.

Adults need to be role models, tasting, describing and encouraging the children to experiment and enjoy a rich and varied diet. It is important to plan carefully and take into account how many adults are available for snack support. If you are short of employed adults in your setting, you could invite parents, other carers and people from the local community to join you.

Some children are cautious of new experiences and will reject them when first presented, but the next time they encounter the taste or texture it will be slightly familiar, eventually tastes are accepted and enjoyed. The ideas in this book used on a daily basis and shared with parents will encourage the children to eat a wide variety of foods presented in a wide variety of ways.

Snack time is an enjoyable, social activity that can aid transition from one type of setting to another. If children are used to exploring and talking about food in a Nursery, then when a similar activity takes place when they begin school it helps them to feel secure, if when they move to key stage one there are elements of snack time during the week then again the children can settle into new routines more confidently. They will understand the expectations of using all their senses and discussing preferences and their learning will be enhanced.

A range of resources, books and web sites to support your work are included at the end of the book.

Health and Safety Issues

Food Allergies

Food intolerance is a general term used to describe a range of unpleasant reactions to food, for a variety of reasons. Some of these reasons are medical and some are allergic. Food allergy happens when the body's immune system over-reacts to a substance, resulting in inflammation, usually in a localised area. An allergic reaction can result in breathing difficulties and a severe reaction may result in anaphylactic shock*.

Although true food intolerance effects only 5-8% of children, and food allergy accounts for 1-2% this, it is vital to ask all parents for information regarding food allergies and intolerance, what their child's reaction may look like and what to do if they have a reaction.

Hygiene

Children and adults handling or preparing the food need to understand basic hygiene considerations. Hand washing should become automatic before preparing food, if children are regularly shown what to do and the reason is explained.

Cutlery, utensils and other equipment should be suitable for child use. Children should learn to use knives as well as forks and spoons, but they could start by using butter knives or other knives with rounded ends. It is just as hygienic to use ceramic or wooden plates and bowls as it is to use plastic, and as a bonus the children are less likely to spin, roll and bang real utensils.

Safety

Knives, juicers, graters etc. need to be used carefully and with adult supervision. It is good practice to have some rules about safety, to teach them as soon as children are able to understand them, and to remind children of them regularly.

*Anaphylactic shock is: A sudden, severe allergic reaction characterised by a sharp drop in blood pressure, and breathing difficulties that is caused by exposure to a foreign substance, such as a drug or bee venom, after a preliminary or sensitising exposure. The reaction may be fatal if emergency treatment, including epinephrine injections, is not given immediately. Also called anaphylaxis. (definition from dictionary.com)

Snack Time and National Priorities

New research projects concerning healthy eating and young children are regularly undertaken and the results being discussed widely. Child health and the future health of nations in the Western World are key topics for discussion in the media and within governments. It is part of professional good practice to keep up with recent thinking by reading, watching TV (over a balanced range of opinion) and using the Internet and keep up to date with new ideas. School and government web sites often have information about projects related to the Healthy Schools Award Scheme.

Health and Education

The importance of good nourishment for babies and young children is well recognised by SureStart, and most local programmes provide advice and information on healthy eating and nutrition for families on low incomes, placing emphasis on the importance of consumption of fruit and vegetables. The proposal to fund Family Centres in all areas will enable this work across a wider range of income and social settings. They will also build on the work done in multi-ethnic communities and with socially isolated groups. It is not only families on low incomes that need advice on healthy eating!

The DFES has recently published the National 5 year Strategy for Education which aims to offer the following:

> 'All parents and families will be able to get one-stop-support at SureStart Children's Centres - with childcare and education, health and employment advice and parenting support on offer together, within easy reach of every parent.
> We know from our analysis that intervening early to give all children the best possible foundation for their learning and development is vital. Early years interventions have been shown to lead to improved health, early development and readiness for school, better relationships between parents and children, and improved social and emotional development.'

And

> 'Our aim is that every school should be a healthy school, giving good teaching and advice about nutrition and exercise backed up by its school lunches, by its PE and school sport, and by its playground activities. Through this work, we will tackle levels of obesity in children, aiming to halt the growth in obesity among under-11s by 2010.' (DFES 5 year strategy)

14

Parents

Current research into the influence of parents on children's diets, and the change in family eating habits has resulted in much media interest. It is therefore important to keep parents informed of what you are doing in your setting to promote healthy eating, and why you see this as an important part of your job. It is a good idea to have a list of the foods the children are currently eating available for the parents, so they know what their child is talking about and can ask for more information if they wish.

Parents need the message that snack time is an opportunity for their child to try different foods with friends in an educational environment, while learning about the positive effects different types of food have for their health and growth. Parents could also be involved in cooking activities, bringing in special food related to cultural celebrations and their family preferences.

> Children should never be given the impression that their parents are giving them the wrong food to eat at home.

Obesity

Obesity is on the increase in this country, and childhood obesity is more common now than it has ever been. A recent report on Child Obesity by the Department of Health discusses how the causes of obesity are part of the norms of society and that there is no one simple solution. The Royal College of Physicians, Royal Collage of Pediatrics and Child Health, and the Faculty of Public Health have emphasised the need for solutions to be:

> 'long term and sustainable, recognising that behaviour change is complex, difficult and takes time.'

The report notes that although individuals will have a key role in their own health and lifestyle it is important that obesity is tackled at a societal level. This is one of the reasons why healthy eating in a social situation is an effective way to develop children's health.

The report comments on how understanding the importance of healthy eating is of no use to children if they do not have the skill to put their knowledge into practice. They praise the 'Cooking Bus' *(see end of book for contact details),* and similar projects but point out that:

> 'Learning about how to choose and prepare healthy meals should be an integral part of every young persons education"

The report states that the Healthy Schools initiatives have resulted in children gaining a deeper understanding when they grow their own food as this helps their understanding of where food comes from as well as motivating them to try different vegetables.

The report also emphasises the importance of involving teachers, governors, parents and the children when devising school healthy eating and nutrition policies. The government needs to accept the seriousness of the problem for if the rise in obesity continues future generations will have shorter life expectancies than their parents.

Nutrition, Health and the curriculum

Healthy eating features in curriculum guidance for every stage.

In Birth to Three Matters

The Birth to Three Framework of effective practice is constructed around four aspects:

A Strong Child; A Skillful Communicator; A Competent Learner and A Healthy Child.

A Healthy Child in Birth to Three is about more than eating nutritious food, it is about emotional well being, growing and developing, keeping safe and healthy choices.

On the component card (one of 16 cards giving guidance to practitioners) for Healthy Choices the Framework states,

> 'From birth, young babies show preferences for people and for what they want to see, hear and taste.'

Children are continually exploring and discovery what they like and dislike, and as practitioners, teachers, parents or carers we need to support this by giving opportunities for children to make real choices. Even the youngest children need appropriate control over their environment and most definitely over what goes into their body.

The ideas and activities in this book are concerned with healthy eating choices, and if variety can be introduced at an early age, with real choices and time to talk about their choice, children will accept that trying something new and then forming an opinion is an important and valued part of everyday life.

In the Foundation Stage Curriculum

If children between the ages of three and six are given the opportunity to sit in a small group in a social situation, they will naturally practice and learn social and communication skills. Using the social occasion of eating and drinking creates more learning opportunities, children learn about:

- food from around the world;
- other cultures;
- what everyday food is made out of;
- the range and diversity of food and taste;
- the use of mathematical language and skills for sorting out simple problems;
- how different foods affect the human body;
- that other people may like different things;
- that they can try new things;
- using their senses and developing independence skills.

Many of the snack ideas in this book also give opportunities for counting for a purpose. Asking the children to only take a piece of food if there are enough for all the children to have a piece; asking them to take a specific number; or asking the children to take as many pieces as the claps /drum beats they hear, reinforces counting for a real purpose and gives children the opportunity to practice their counting skills.

Some snack ideas lend themselves to other areas of the curriculum and these are included on the snack activity pages. However there are some areas of the curriculum that will be developed through every snack time, and some of these are listed below:

Communication, Language and Literacy - Language for communication

Yellow stepping stone - Use isolated words and phrases and/or gestures to communicate with those well known to them.

Yellow stepping stone - Use words and/or gestures to communicate

Yellow stepping stone - Respond to simple instructions

Yellow stepping stone - Use familiar words, often in isolation, to identify what they do and do not want

Blue stepping stone - Use a widening range of words to express ideas.

Blue stepping stone - Use a widening range of words to express or elaborate ideas

Blue stepping stone - Question why things happen and give explanations

Blue stepping stone - Build up vocabulary that reflects the breadth of their experience

Green stepping stone - Use language for an increasing range of purposes.

Green stepping stone - Initiate a conversation, negotiate positions, pay attention to and take account of other's views.

Green stepping stone - Extend vocabulary, especially by grouping and naming
Early Learning Goal - Speak clearly and audibly with confidence and control and show awareness of the listener, for example, by their use of conventions such as 'please' and 'thank you'.
Early Learning Goal - Interact with others, negotiating plans and activities, taking turns in conversation
Early Learning Goal - Enjoy listening to and using spoken and written language.
Early Learning Goal - Extend their vocabulary, exploring the meanings and sounds of new words

Communication, Language and Literacy - Language for thinking
Yellow stepping stone - Use action, sometimes with limited talk, that is largely concerned with the 'here & now'
Yellow stepping stone - Have a positive approach to new experiences
Blue stepping stone - Use talk to connect ideas, explain what is happening and anticipate what might happen next
Blue stepping stone - Show increasing confidence in selecting and carrying out activities
Green stepping stone - Use language for an increasing range of purposes.
Green stepping stone - Initiate a conversation, negotiate positions, pay attention to and take account of other's views.
Green stepping stone - Extend vocabulary, especially by grouping and naming
Early Learning Goal - Use talk to organise, sequence and clarify thinking, ideas, feelings and events

Personal, Social and Emotional Development - Dispositions and attitudes
Yellow stepping stone - Have a positive approach to new experiences
Green stepping stone - Display high levels of involvement in activities
Early Learning Goal - Be confident to try new activities, initiate ideas and speak in a familiar group

Personal, Social and Emotional Development - Self Confidence and Self Esteem
Blue stepping stone - Talk freely about their home and community
Green stepping stone - Initiate interactions with other people
Early Learning Goal - Have a developing awareness of their own needs, views and feelings and be sensitive to the needs, views and feelings of others

Personal, Social and Emotional Development - Making Relationships
Yellow stepping stone - Seek out others to share experiences
Blue stepping stone - Demonstrate flexibility and adapt their behaviour to different events, social situations and changes in routine
Green stepping stone - Value and contribute to their own well-being and self-control
Early Learning Goal - Work as part of a group or class, taking turns and sharing fairly.

Physical Development - Health and Bodily Awareness
Yellow stepping stone - Show awareness of own needs with regard to eating and hygiene
Blue stepping stone - Show awareness of a range of healthy practices
Green stepping stone - Show some understanding that good practices can relate to good health
Early Learning Goal - Recognise the importance of keeping healthy and those things which contribute to this.

In the National Curriculum at Key Stage One

The language and social skills developed and practiced through a snack time activity are still of great importance to children in Key Stage One. If they are offered healthy snack time at this stage, they will be able to continue their knowledge of food and begin to explore health issues in more detail. Snack time is a good opportunity to develop the children's learning in a familiar social situation

Aspects of English, mathematics and science can be taught through snack time, and these are included on the snack activity pages. In addition to these objectives it is important to look at the breadth of study for English, Mathematics and Science, as these are concerned with the context of learning rather than the objectives.

English

Breadth of study - speaking; During the key stage pupils should be taught knowledge, skills and understanding through
- 8c describing events and experiences
- 9a listen to each other
- 10a making plans and investigation
- 10b sharing ideas and experiences
- 10c commenting and reporting

Breadth of study - reading; During the key stage pupils should be taught knowledge, skills and understanding through
- 7a print and ICT texts
- 7b dictionaries, encyclopedias and other reference materials

Breadth of study - writing; During the key stage pupils should be taught knowledge, skills and understanding through
- 9a to communicate to others
- 9c to explore experience
- 9d to organise and explain information
- 10 for remembering and developing ideas
- 11 range of readers for writing
- 12 range of forms - notes, lists, captions, poems, records, instructions

Mathematics

Breadth of Study; During the key stage pupils should be taught knowledge, skills and understanding through
- A practical activity, exploration and discussion
- B using mathematical ideas in practical activities, then recording these using objects, pictures, diagrams, words, numbers and symbols.
- E drawing inferences from data in practical activities

Science

Breadth of Study; During the key stage pupils should be taught knowledge, skills and understanding through

A   a range of domestic and environmental contexts that are familiar and of interest to them

D   using first-hand and secondary data to carry out a range of scientific investigations.

Objective Specific Snack Time

Some people like to link snack time with a particular curriculum area such as Mathematical Development, Personal, Social and Emotional Development or Knowledge and Understanding of the World. These teachers may have a specific time of the day when everyone sits down for snacks together, then with some adult input, open questioning or guidance the children will try different foods with their peers. This session usually lasts about 15 minutes and the adults have the specific curriculum objectives in mind or on a board, and focus their support and questions around these.

For example - focusing on Knowledge and Understanding of the World

Objective: Blue stepping stone; Describe simple features

Weekly Session Plan

- ✏ Each day of the week, have two contrasting size fruit.
- ✏ Ask the children to pass the fruit around whole and discuss colour, size, shape, texture, smell - some of these words could be written on a large picture of the fruits of the day.
- ✏ Ask the children to guess what the fruit may look like inside.
- ✏ Cut the fruit and invite each child to take a piece to put on their plate.
- ✏ Encourage the children to look, smell and lick the fruit - they do not have to eat it (try to offer some fruit they will eat as well)
- ✏ Children who do want to eat it can then eat their piece and have more.
- ✏ Encourage the children to talk about what they like/dislike about the fruit.
- ✏ Establish a rota for collecting and washing the plates and cups.

The session could then be followed up with a series of activities around the room:

- ✋ Pictures of fruit to sort for size/ shape/ like and dislike etc
- ✋ Making a chart of likes and dislikes
- ✋ Clay/dough to make the fruit they like, finding tools to make the skin texture feel the same.

General Snack Time rules

These rules, or some you have devised yourself, preferably with the children are useful to ensure consistency and a healthy approach:

- We talk about the food.

- We look at the food.

- We feel the food.

- We smell the food.

- We taste the food.

- We do not have to eat the whole snack.

- We can say whether we like the food or not.

- We only take a snack food if there is enough for everyone to have a piece.

Snack type: Fruit

Activity: Looking at colour

What you need: Each day of week have a different colour focus;

Yellow - banana, lemon, melon, grapefruit, star fruit

Green - apple, lime, pear, greengage, mango, water-melon, kiwi, gooseberry, ugli fruit, grapes,

Orange - orange, tangerine, Sharon fruit, peach, pineapple, kumquat

Purple - grapes, plum, passion fruit, fresh fig, (blackcurrant)

Red - redcurrants, strawberries, raspberries, apples, persimmons, cherries, pomegranates, cranberries

What you do:

1. Try to have more than one fruit of each colour on each day. This will enable you to talk about colours and shades of different fruits.
2. Wash the fruit carefully.
3. Sit with the children and look at the fruit. It may be best to pass berries and softer fruit round in a small bowl or on a plate.
4. Feel the surface of the fruits gently, smell them, talk about the skins texture.
5. Now cut some of the big fruits open to see what is inside. Talk about stones, seeds and pips. Some fruits have their pips and seeds on the outside. Talk about the flesh of the fruit.
6. Now cut the fruit into suitable pieces and offer it to the children to taste. Remind them that they don't have to eat a whole piece of a new fruit, just taste it.

Extensions and follow up ideas:

* Compare the fruit colours. Are all the yellows/reds/purples exactly the same? What is different?
* Can you find the same shade of the 'colour of the day' somewhere in the room or outside?
* Use of paint colour shade cards/shades of colour to find similar colours in the environment.
* Try making the same colours with a computer paint programme, then use computer software to draw and colour fruit pictures
* Find a computer programme with a fruit sorting game.
* Make up fruit poems linked to their colour
* Experiment with mixing colours in paint. Try adding small amounts of white or black to paint colours and talking about what happens.
* Paint, draw, or make fruit shapes with dough. Try to make the correct shade.
* Write words used to describe the colours on big pictures of the fruit.
* Take photos of the fruit and make a 'Snack Scrap Book'. Add pictures cut from magazines, supermarket leaflets and children's drawings and words.

Stepping Stones and Goals:

Knowledge and Understanding of the World; Exploration and Investigation:

Yellow - Explore objects

Blue - Describe simple features

Green - Examine objects and living things to find out more about them

Early Learning Goals - Look closely at similarities, differences, pattern and change
Investigate objects and materials with all of their senses as appropriate

Key Stage One Science:

Sc1f - Explore, using the senses of sight, hearing, smell, touch and taste as appropriate, and make and record observations and measurements

Snack type: Fruit

Activity: Looking at size and shape

What you need: each day of week have fruit of differing sizes;

Small - cumquat, fresh currants, grapes, fresh berries

Medium - apples, tangerines, pears, passion fruit, persimmon, Sharon fruit, kiwi, banana

Large - melon, pineapple, mango, pawpaw, grapefruit, coconut, ugli fruit

What you do:

1. Try to have contrasting size fruits on each day. Ideally you could have fruits of the same general colour, as this will help the children to concentrate on the size. This will enable you to talk about colours and shades of different fruits.
2. Wash the fruit carefully.
3. Sit with the children and look at the fruit you have chosen. It may be best to pass berries and softer fruit round in a small bowl or on a plate.
4. Feel the surface of the fruits gently, smell them, talk about the skins texture.
5. Now talk about the different sizes of the fruit you have chosen. Don't just look at bigger and smaller, make sure you extend your vocabulary to comparatives such as 'big, bigger, biggest', 'small, smaller, smallest'.
6. Cut some of the fruit in half to see what is inside. If you have comparable fruit such as a tangerine and a grapefruit, compare the size of the segments, the thickness of the skin, the size of the pips, stones and seeds.
7. Taste the fruit, but remind children they don't have to eat it all.

Extensions and follow up ideas:

* Try cutting the fruit into different sized slices. Ask the children if they want a bigger or smaller slice than the child before.
* Count how many fruit portions you can get out of a whole fruit. Try this with small, medium and large fruits.
* Measure length, width, and circumference with string. ribbon or a tape measure.
* Have pictures or real fruit to sort for size or shape.
* Use a digital camera to photograph the fruit and then use a computer to make small and large copies of the photos.
* Tell the Three Bear's story, then use other toys to sort for size.
* Suggest some ideas for problem solving using measuring and size, eg making bags for 3 apples; chairs for different size bears; different size notebooks.
* Make posting boxes for different size and shape parcels.
* Offer some measuring activities with string, ribbons, tapes etc.
* Make a bag or box with measuring tools, note pad, pen etc. to use outside.
* Older children could extend their knowledge with some work on simple fractions - halves, quarters, thirds.

Stepping Stones and Goals:

Mathematical Development; Number; Shape, Space and Measures:

Yellow - Show an interest in counting

Blue - Begin to talk about the shapes of everyday objects

Green - Count, saying one number for each item up to 6; Order items by length

Early Learning Goals - Use language such as circle, or bigger to describe the shape and size of solids

Key Stage One Mathematics:

Ma3 b - select and use appropriate mathematical equipment when solving problems involving measures or measurement

Ma3 d - use the correct language and vocabulary for shape, space and measures

Snack type: Fruit

Activity: Looking at pips and stones

What you need: each day of week have different fruit with pips/seeds and stones

Pips/seeds - apple, orange, lemon, lime, grapefruit, passion fruit, kiwi, melon, grapes, pear, berries, watermelon, fig, strawberry (pips on the outside), banana

Stones - mango, peach, nectarine, plum, cherry, apricot, date, avocado

What you do:

1. Try to have fruit with <u>either</u> pips or stones on each day. This will help children to understand the difference between pips and stones. Stones have a hard coating to protect the seed, pips have a coating that softens as the seed sprouts.
2. Wash the fruit carefully.
3. Sit with the children and look at the fruit you have chosen. It may be best to pass berries and softer fruit round in a small bowl or on a plate.
4. Feel the surface of the fruits gently, smell them, talk about the skins texture.
5. Now look at the fruits that have seeds or pips on the outside. Gently take some off and look at them (with a magnifying glass if you have one).
6. Now talk about where the seeds, pips or stones might be in the other fruit. Cut some in half to see what you can find. Look carefully at the seeds, pips and stones you find. Feel them between your fingers, talk about whether the flesh comes away easily or sticks to the fruit. Older children may be ready to explore what the flesh of the fruit is for (protection and food for a growing plant).
7. Taste the fruit, reminding children they don't have to eat it all.

Extensions and follow up ideas:

* Guess whether the fruit will have pips or a stone.
* Try cracking the seeds and stones so you can look at the seeds inside.
* Count the pips and stones you find, and make a chart of the numbers you find (even two different melons will have different numbers of seeds!). You could stick the pips or seeds to the chart to make a pictorial graph.
* Plant pips and stones, write labels, water and watch to see if they grow.
* Make an information poster chart with pictures of fruit and the seeds that have been washed and dried.
* Look at and make books about growing things (The Little Book of Growing Things has lots of ideas).
* Make picture or photo sequences of plant growth.
* Find seeds from other plants to look at, play with, make patterns with, sort, count. Use rice, beans, lentils and other dried foods - talk about them first so children know they are all seeds.
* Go on a seed-collecting walk (late summer or autumn is best, but weeds seed all the year round). Look at different sorts of seed heads and pods.
* Compare flower seeds and seeds from trees and other plants, grasses etc.

Stepping Stones and Goals:

Mathematical Development; Number; Shape, Space and Measures:

Yellow - Show an interest in counting; Use size language such as big and little

Blue - Begin to talk about the shapes of everyday objects

Green - Count, saying one number for each item up to 6; Order items by length

Early Learning Goals - Use language such as circle, or bigger to describe shape and size

Key Stage One Mathematics:

Sc2 3a - to recognise that plants need light and water to grow

Sc2 3c - that seeds grow into flowering plants

Sc2 4b - group living things according to observable similarities and differences

Snack type: Fruit

Activity: Looking at inside and outside

What you need: each day of week have at least two varieties of fruit, for example:

Contrasting colours inside and out - Pink grapefruit, mangoes, apples, passion fruit, watermelons, bananas

Fruit with segments - oranges, lemons, grapefruit, tangerines

Fruit with thick skins - pineapples, passion fruit

Fruit with thin skins - apples, grapes, blackcurrants

Fruit with smooth skins - apples, grapes, bananas, plums, cherries

Fruit with hairy or lumpy skins - kiwi fruit, peaches, apricots, lychees, melons, gooseberries

What you do:

1. Try to have contrasting fruits on each day, and ideally have more than one of each type.

2. Wash the fruit carefully and let them dry, specially the hairy ones.

3. Sit with the children and look at the fruit you have chosen. Pass the fruit round so the children can feel the skins of each fruit. Guess whether the skins are thin or thick, describe them using expressive words, and encouraging the children to expand their use of descriptive words.

4. Feel the surface of the fruits gently, smell them, talk about the skin's texture.

5. If you have several different fruits, and older children, sort the fruits as many ways as you can - size, shape, colour as well as texture. Remember, younger children will find this too difficult and confusing!

6. Cut some of the fruit in half and compare the inside and the outside before you eat them! Remind the children about tasting new things.

Extensions and follow up ideas:

* Make a drawing table with fruit to draw, whole and cut. Provide a variety of media - paint, pastels, crayons, computer as well as a variety of fruit.
* Offer clay or dough to make fruit, whole and cut. Talk about what to use to make patterns for skin, segments, cores, pips etc. Look together to find things that make textures, eg net bags, fabrics, nail brushes, forks.
* Find lots of pictures of fruit in magazines and leaflets, and make pictures and scrapbooks of fruit.
* Make up a story about travelling through a piece of fruit - use the Hungry Caterpillar video as a stimulus.
* Do printing with fruit. Use the activity to work on repeating patterns. If you feel uncomfortable using real fruit, make some sponge shapes of fruits.
* Make a fruit shop or market stall and sell real or pretend fruit. This is a great activity for outdoors.
* Have feely boxes or bags with fruits inside - can they guess what fruit is inside?

Stepping Stones and Goals:

> Knowledge and Understanding of the World; Exploration and Investigation
> Yellow - Show curiosity
> Blue - Describe simple features
> Green - Examine objects and living things to find out more about them.
> Early Learning Goals - Investigate objects by using all of their senses as appropriate

Key Stage One Science:

> Sc1 1 - Pupils should be taught that it is important to collect evidence by making observations and measurements when trying to answer a question

Key Stage One Art and Design:

> 4a - Pupils should be taught about visual and tactile elements, including colour, pattern, texture, line and tone, form and space

Snack type: Fruit

Activity: Where does it come from?

What you need: Each day of week, have fruit from two different parts of the world

Tropical - tropical fruit such as mangoes, lychees, pineapples, bananas, kiwi fruit, pawpaws

European - fruit which is familiar to most children, such as apples, pears and oranges

Seasonal - fruit which grows in the UK in summer, but is available all the year round by import. These fruits include grapes, strawberries, raspberries, blueberries. When working with older children, in Reception and KS1, you also need a globe or world atlas. Younger children find it really difficult to get the concept of other countries, even if they have been abroad on holiday; they would be better looking at a book of other countries or the fruits growing in their native lands.

What you do:

1. Try to have fruits from two groups on each day.
2. Wash the fruit carefully.
3. Sit with the children and look at the fruit you have chosen.
4. Try to guess where they grow. Do they grow on trees? bushes? plants?
5. Talk about the places where fruit grows and that different fruit grows in different countries.
6. Read a book such as Handa's Surprise, or Oliver's Fruit Salad and talk about the different fruit.
7. Taste the different fruit as you imagine the places where they grow.

Extensions and follow up ideas:

* Older children may like to guess where the fruits grow. Or they may know from their own families where the fruit comes from.
* Make some little flags with pictures of the fruit and stick them in a map or globe in the country where they grow. Look at books about the countries where the fruit comes from. Put up some posters about fruit and where it grows.
* Discuss how some fruit is grown in our country but only in greenhouses where it is warm, while other sorts (our native fruits) grow out of doors.
* Make charts to show the children's likes and dislikes.
* Use a computer graphing programme to find out each others' likes and dislikes.
* Set up some problem solving tasks in the small world area or water tray - have different islands or countries with fruit, how will the people transport fruit to other islands?
* Set up a fruit shop or market stall indoors or outside, with boxes and bags, and perhaps a truck for transporting the fruit from a farm to a shop.
* Try growing some fruit, some indoors, some outside, or in a mini greenhouse - keep observation logs of the plants to see where they grow the best, using digital cameras, observational drawings, labelled diagrams and notes.

Stepping Stones and Goals:

Knowledge and Understanding of the World; A sense of place

Yellow - Show an interest in the world in which they live

Blue - Comment on and ask questions about the natural world

Green - Gain an awareness of the cultures of others

Early Learning Goals - Find out about their environment

Key Stage One Science:

Sc2 3a - recognise that plants need light and water to grow

Sc2 3b - to recognise and name the leaf, flower, stem and root of flowering plants

Sc2 3c - that seeds grow into flowering plants

Snack type: Fruit

Activity: Exploring dried and fresh

What you need: from Monday to Thursday have fresh and dried versions of one fruit each day, then have them all on Friday

Try some of these - pear, apple, banana, dried and fresh
Or - raisins/currants/sultanas and fresh grapes
Or - dried and fresh blueberries and cranberries

What you do:

1. Put some of the dried fruit on a plate and let the children look at it to guess what the fresh fruit version is. Talk about how fruit is dried, either by putting it in the sun or by drying it in an oven.

2. Now look at the fresh version and talk about the difference. What is different? What has happened? How does the dried fruit look and feel different? Older children may be able to think about why drying fruit is a good idea.

3. Now you can each take some of each version to taste.

4. Talk about the version the children like best.

5. Taste the fruit, but remind children they don't have to eat it all.

Extensions and follow up ideas:

* Put up a chart of likes and dislikes, dried or fresh, or favourite fruits.
* Help the children to take digital photos, draw pictures of the fruit dry and fresh. Make an interactive display with the pictures and ribbons. Can they match the dried and fresh fruits?
* Put dried fruit into water; ask the children to guess what may happen, then watch and record.
* Use a drum to signal the number of raisins etc they can take from the plate.
* Sing 'Five Currant Buns'; make a baker's shop for role play.
* Make muesli bars (there's a recipe at the end of the book).

Explore drying and re-hydrating:

* Challenge them to find out what material dries up spilt water best.
* Look at different climates and compare the extremes of wet and dry.
* Compare animals that live in water and those which live on land.
* Provide opportunities for exploring dry substances and what happens to them when you add water - try cornflour, sand, soil, powder paint, flour, cocoa powder, milk shake. (remind them not to taste these!)

Stepping Stones and Goals:

Knowledge and Understanding of the World; Observation and investigation

Yellow - Show curiosity

Blue -   Talk about what is seen and what is happening

Green - Show an awareness of change

Early Learning Goals - Ask questions about why things happen and how things work

Key Stage One Science:

Sc1 f - explore, using the senses of sight, hearing, smell, touch and taste as appropriate, and make and record observations and measurements.

Snack type: **Fruit**

Activity: **Looking at canned and fresh**

What you need: from Monday to Thursday, have tinned & fresh versions of one fruit, then make fruit salad on Friday

Make sure the fruit is tinned in fruit juice, not syrup.

Suggested fruits - pineapple, pears, peaches, grapes, strawberries, gooseberries, cherries, blackberries

What you do:

1. Before you open the canned fruit, look at the can together and see what the children can find out before you open the can. What is inside? How did it get in there. Where did it come from?
2. Open the can and tip the fruit into a bowl.
3. Pass the bowl round so everyone can see and smell the fruit.
4. Talk about what it looks like.
5. Now look at the fresh version. Does it look like the canned version? Talk about why that could be. Look for peel, talk about differences in colour, texture, shape.
6. Taste some of each, canned and fresh. Now talk about the flavour and texture. Which do they like best? Remind children they don't have to eat it all.
7. Make a chart with a picture of a can and a picture of the fresh fruit. Let the children make a mark, write their name or use a stamp and pad to record their favourite.

Extensions and follow up ideas:

* On Friday have a range of fresh and canned fruits and let the children make fruit salads with their favourites. Take photos of the final salads and the children could write their ingredients for a fruit salad display or a recipe book.
* Design labels for fruit tins. How can they make them irresistible to shoppers?
* Set up a supermarket with empty cans and home made labels.
* Talk about why fruit is tinned - to keep it fresh for longer; to stop it getting damaged; to transport it.
* Older children could give points out of 10 for texture and taste for tinned and fresh fruit - record this and display.
* Ask children to find out what fresh and tinned fruit their parents or grandparents ate when they were young.
* Set up experiments to see how long fresh fruit lasts before going mouldy. Compare with 'best before' dates on the cans.
* Discuss different likes and dislikes between people, and how it is OK to be different.

Stepping Stones and Goals:

Knowledge and Understanding of the World; Observation and Investigation

Yellow - Show curiosity

Blue - Talk about what is seen and what is happening

Green - Show an awareness of change

Early Learning Goals - Ask questions about why things happen and how things work

Key Stage One Science:

Sc1 f - explore, using the senses of sight, hearing, smell, touch and taste as appropriate, and make and record observations and measurements

Snack type: Fruit

Activity: All mixed up in a fruit salad

What you need: a variety of fruit each day

    Some suggestions - grapes, apples, bananas,
                      pears, tangerines, kiwi fruit
                      and - fruit juice

    Other equipment - bowls, chopping boards, round
                      ended knives, forks, spoons

What you do:

1. Children should be encouraged to do as much of this as possible, making their own salads each day. For younger children you could chop separate fruits into bowls and children can spoon out their own choice. However, even very young children can chop their own fruit if they are given the chance to be independent. You could halve the fruit and then spear a half on a fork to make cutting easier for them, staying close to give help if they need it.
2. Wash the fruit carefully, and make a welcoming place for children to sit and eat their creations.
3. Talk with the children about the different fruits as they choose their favourites, peel them (if necessary) and chop them for their own salad.
4. Talk as they work about only taking a fair share, and only taking what they can eat.
5. When they have made their salad, let them choose to pour a little juice over it before eating.
6. Encourage them to make a different salad every day from a slightly different range of fruits.

Extensions and follow up ideas:

* Have a self serve cafe where children can choose their own mixture from ready prepared fruits and juices.
* Challenge older children to make a different salad each day and photograph it for a display.
* Talk about different textures and flavours.
* Children can draw pictures of their fruit salad and invent a name.
* Have fruit in the domestic role play area, and add examples of fruit salad recipes and recipe cards so the children can make their own pretend food.
* Use the photos to make adverts, recipe book, recipe cards.
* Discuss different likes and dislikes in class and how it is OK to be different.
* Make a photo sequence or a Power Point presentation of how to make a fruit salad.

Stepping Stones and Goals:

Mathematical Development; Number; Shape, Space and Measures:

Yellow - Show curiosity

Blue -   Talk about what is seen and what is happening

Green - Show an awareness of change

Early Learning Goals - Ask questions about why things happen and how things work

Key Stage One Science:

Sc1 f -   explore, using the senses of sight, hearing, smell, touch and taste as appropriate, and make and record observations and measurements

Snack type: Fruit/vegetables

Activity: Fruit and vegetable kebabs

What you need: a range of fruit & vegetables

Fruit -   cubes of apple or pineapple, tangerine
           segments, banana slices, grapes, blueber-
           ries, cherries

Vegetables - cucumber, courgettes, carrots, sweet
           corn, peas, baby tomatoes, radishes

You also need - bowls, wooden skewers, plain yogurt to dip

What you do:

1. Let the children help to prepare the fruit and vegetables.
2. Wash the fruit carefully.
3. Sit with the children and look at the fruit you have chosen. It may be best to
    pass berries and softer fruit round in a small bowl or on a plate.
4. Feel the surface of the fruits gently, smell them, talk about the skins texture.
5. Now talk about the different sizes of the fruit you have chosen. Don't just
    look at bigger and smaller, help them to extend their vocabulary to comparatives
    such as 'big, bigger, biggest', 'small, smaller, smallest'.
6. Cut some of the fruit in half to see what is inside. If you have comparable
    fruit such as a tangerine and a grapefruit, compare the size of the segments,
    the thickness of the skin, the size of the pips, stones and seeds.
7. Taste the fruit, but remind children they don't have to eat it all.

Extensions and follow up ideas:

* Younger children could just make patterns of fruit pieces on a plate or polystyrene tray. They don't need to use a skewer until they can manage it.
* Offer just three different types and see how many different patterns children can make on their skewers.
* Be on hand to help children compare what they have chosen.
* Count how many pieces they have, eat one and count again (great practice for 'one less'!).
* Estimate/guess how many pieces they can fit on their kebab, then count to see if they guessed correctly.
* Talk about different textures and flavours.
* Look at pictures and books about fruit and vegetables.
* Make pretend kebabs out of recycled materials, clay etc and set up a kebab shop, make price lists, posters and advertising for the shop.
* Talk about why fruit and vegetables are needed as part of a healthy diet
* Make charts, lists of the most popular foods chosen

Stepping Stones and Goals:

Mathematical Development; Number; Shape, Space and Measures:

Yellow - Use some number names and number language spontaneously

Blue - Willingly attempt to count, with some numbers in the correct order

Green - Count up to three or four objects by saying one number name for each item

Early Learning Goals - Count reliably up to ten everyday objects.

Key Stage One Mathematics:

Ma2 5a - solve a relevant problem by using simple lists, tables and charts to sort, classify and organise information

Key Stage One Science:

Sc1 f- explore, using the senses of sight, hearing, smell, touch and taste as appropriate, and make and record observations and measurements

Snack type: Fruit/vegetables

Activity: Juicing

What you need: a range of fruit & vegetables suitable for juicing

Suitable Fruit - oranges, apples, pears, pineapple, strawberries

Suitable Vegetables - carrots

You also need - mugs or beakers, knife, juicing machine

(you could use an old fashioned lemon or orange squeezer if you haven't got a juicer)

What you do:

1. You could chop some of the fruit/vegetables before you start the activity, leaving some whole for the children to see before chopping and juicing.
2. Wash the fruit/vegetables carefully.
3. Sit with the children and look at the fruit you have chosen. Feel and smell it.
4. Now chop the fruit ready for juicing (different juicing machines require different preparation. Read the instructions first!).
5. Talk about what happens when juice is made. Look at what comes out of the juicer and what is left behind. Older children need to begin to understand that the bit left behind is very good for your body, and that juice is not as good for you as the whole fruit.
6. Taste the different juices you have made, and offer some shop bought alternatives to extend children's repertoire.
7. Always emphasise the importance of tasting new foods and drinks.

Extensions and follow up ideas:

* Discuss what the fruit is like inside, ask children if they think the fruit will have a lot of juice inside or just a little.
* Ask children to guess what colour the juice will be, older children could record their predictions.
* Discuss likes and dislikes, and favourites.
* look at the colour of the juice and compere it with the fruit.
* Set up a juice bar. The children can advertise, set prices and try out different flavours together.
* Invite other children or parents to the juice bar.
* Children could do a survey of favourite drinks, hot and cold.
* Provide opportunities for experimenting with mixing colours - coloured water, colour paddles, cellophane, paint.

Stepping Stones and Goals:

Knowledge and Understanding of the World: Exploration and investigation
Yellow - Show curiosity
Blue - Talk about what is seen and what is happening
Green - Show an awareness of change
Early Learning Goals - Ask questions about why things happen and how things work.

Key Stage One Science:

1a - study a range of domestic and environmental contexts that are familiar and of interest to them.

Snack type: Bread

Activity: All sorts of bread

What you need: a range of different breads

    Suggestions - French bread, brioche, wholemeal, multigrain, croissant, white, chappatti, naan, rolls, fruit or malt loaf (supermarket bakeries offer a huge range)

    You also need - plate, round ended knives, soft butter or other spread, bread board or other clean cutting board, a globe or world map for older children

What you do:

1. It's better to get two or three different breads each day. This way, children don't get overwhelmed with the different flavours and types.
2. Introduce the topic of bread, talk with the children about what it is, when they eat it, what sorts of bread they like, how it is made.
3. Look at the bread together before you cut it. Pass it round on a board or in a basket so the children can smell it without handling it. Talk about the different breads, where they are from and the different smells, shapes and textures.
4. Cut the bread into small pieces for the children to choose and taste.
5. Look carefully at the texture inside each type of bread. Look for grains, talk about the holes in the bread and how they got there.
6. Let the children spread the pieces of bread themselves.
7. Take photos of each sort of bread you try, it will help the children to remember the names and flavours.

* Always check for gluten allergy or sensitivity before offering grain based food.

42

Extensions and follow up ideas:

* Tell them the name of each bread and write a list - add bread names to this list as week goes on.
* Talk about bread, and write some of their descriptive words on bread shaped posters.
* Offer them soft butter and margarine, so they can choose which to spread on their bread tasters.
* Make some bread (there is a recipe in the Little Book of Cooking from Stories).
* Look on the map or globe of the world. Take photos of the different bread and put them on the map or globe.
* Make some play dough, put it in the home corner so children can make pretend bread and rolls.
* Look at and make books about bread.
* Make a graph or chart of who likes which bread. You could put a photo of each bread down one side of the chart and children's names down the other side. Children could then use a thick marker to join their name to the bread(s) they like.
* Find out about types of grain and seeds used in the different breads
* Set up a sandwich bar
* Cut sandwiches into triangles, squares and rectangles.

Stepping Stones and Goals:

Knowledge and Understanding of the World: Exploration and investigation

Yellow - Show curiosity

Blue - Show curiosity, observe and manipulate objects

Green - Examine objects to find out more about them

Early Learning Goals - Look closely at similarities and differences, patterns and change

Key Stage One Geography:

3e - recognise how places are linked to other places in the world - Food from other countries

Snack type: Bread

Activity: Sandwich making

What you need: bread - brown, white, whole grain (sliced or not)

Savoury fillings - mashed tuna, hard boiled egg & mayonnaise, Marmite, ham, cucumber, grated cheese, soft cheese, sliced tomato, hummus

Sweet fillings - honey, jam, fruit spread, mashed banana

You also need - plates, bowls, bread knife, round ended knives, soft butter/spread, bread board or clean boards

What you do:

1. Slice the bread if you need to and offer children a choice. Younger children may manage half slices better than whole ones.
2. Talk about the different sorts of bread, what they look, smell and feel like.
3. Look at the fillings you are offering. Pass them round in bowls so the children can look at them. If there are unfamiliar fillings, let them try a bit on a teaspoon.
4. If the children have not made sandwiches before, you may need to show them how to do it before letting them make their own.
5. Be around to help and talk them through this activity, but let them do it themselves. Even very young children can make their own sandwiches. They may be a bit untidy, but they will love the sense of achievement.
6. Children may also like strange combinations of fillings, don't restrict their sense of adventure! They may invent the next world favourite, or at least expand their own willingness to try new things.

* Always check for gluten allergy or sensitivity before offering grain based food.

Extensions and follow up ideas:

* Practice using polite language to ask for toppings to be passed.
* Discuss their likes and dislikes
* Encourage them to try things that they have not tried before
* Explain the safety aspects of using knives to spread
* Explain the hygiene aspect of hands and mouths, not licking knives or fingers.
* Discuss healthy eating, and healthier sandwiches. Remember, young children need energy, so things that adults need to avoid can be eaten as part of a balanced diet by children!
* Continue to offer safe use of knives and in role play, creative activities and construction as well as cooking and snack times.
* Read linked stories such as The Little Red Hen.
* Make bread or rolls. Add your own ingredients to bread dough (cheese, grated onion, seeds, tomato paste etc). Use a bread maker machine or your own oven.
* Visit a bakery. Supermarkets are a good place to try - ask before you go!
* Make a bakers shop. Make some salt dough for the bread and rolls, and bake them hard for strength. You could even make and paint some filled rolls and sandwiches for take-aways (not to eat of course!).

Stepping Stones and Goals:

Physical development

Yellow - Show awareness of own needs with regard to eating and hygiene

Blue - Show awareness of a range of healthy practices

Green - Show some understanding that good practices can relate to good health

Early Learning Goals - Recognise the importance of keeping healthy and those things which contribute to this

Key Stage One Science:

Sc2 2c - that taking exercise and eating the right types and amounts of food help humans to keep healthy

45

Snack type: Bread

Activity: Breadsticks and dips

What you need: a variety of breadsticks and a variety of dips

Suggestions - plain and seeded and flavoured breadsticks

Dips - hummus, plain or savoury yogurt, soft cheese, salsa, cottage cheese, tomato puree or ketchup

You also need - plates, baskets, bowls, small spoons, beakers, containers such as clean plastic carton bottoms

What you do:

1. Unwrap the breadsticks with the children and look at the different sorts and flavours. Break longer sticks into shorter pieces and put them in baskets or in stand them in beakers and pass them round so the children can look at and smell them.
2. Put the dips out in bowls and give each child a small plate or a clean egg box bottom so they can take small quantities of their chosen dips.
3. Pass the dips round so children can spoon a small amount out to try. Remind them that trying is not the same as having to eat it all.
4. Talk about what the dips taste like, encouraging children to have a taste of everything.
5. Take some photos of the activity for a snack scrapbook

* Always check for gluten allergy or sensitivity before offering grain based food.

Extensions and follow up ideas:

* Try making your own dips using yogurt as a base, and adding different flavours, food colourings and chopped or grated vegetables.
* Practice taking turns, and using polite language to ask for things to be passed.
* Discuss likes and dislikes, and good combinations of breadsticks and dips.
* Encourage children to try things that they have not tried before
* Explain the hygiene aspect of hands and mouths, and why they shouldn't put a bitten breadstick back in a shared dip.
* Talk about what is in the dips, and why this is a healthy snack.
* Make charts so children can tally mark their likes. Include breadstick types as well as dips.
* Offer dips and sticks for them to try at different times of the day, and perhaps even outside.

Stepping Stones and Goals:

Physical development

Yellow - Show awareness of own needs with regard to eating and hygiene

Blue -   Show awareness of a range of healthy practices

Green - Show some understanding that good practices can relate to good health

Early Learning Goals - Recognise the importance of keeping healthy and those things which contribute to this

Key Stage One Geography:

Sc2 2c - that taking exercise and eating the right types and amounts of food help humans to keep healthy

Snack type: Bread
Activity: Toasting
What you need: a range of different breads

> Suggestions - sliced and un-sliced bread of several types, rolls, bagels, muffins, crumpets
>
> You also need - plates, round ended knives, soft butter or other spread, toaster or grill, your choice of sweet/savoury toppings (beans, grated cheese, spaghetti, jam, marmalade, paste, Marmite)

What you do:

1. Always reminded children of safety rules when using anything electrical or hot.
2. Look at the things you have brought to toast, and the toppings. Pass them round to look and smell.
3. Talk about what the children think toasting does. Encourage them to talk about the texture, the heat and the smell of toasting. Talk about the times of day and the meals where toast is eaten.
4. Let each child choose what they want to toast (remember, older children can cope with a wider range of choices). You may want to use this activity over several days, so adjust the choices to your individual plans.
5. If you are using a toaster, talk with the children about how it works. Before you plug it in, let the children look inside at the heating elements and the toast slots. If using a grill, let the children look at this before you heat it up.
6. Toast the children's choice and let them spread it themselves, adding their choice of toppings. Warn them that toast gets hot!

* Always check for gluten allergy or sensitivity before offering grain based food.

Extensions and follow up ideas:

* Use pastry cutters to make toast shapes, animals, numbers.
* Use a sandwich toaster to make toasted sandwiches.
* Encourage children to try things that they have not tried before.
* Explain the safety aspects of using knives for cutting and spreading.
* Explain the hygiene rules of not licking knives or fingers.
* Talk about how different breads change when they are toasted.
* Make charts and graphs with picture, names, photos to record likes and dislikes.
* Discuss healthy eating options.
* Make pretend sandwiches and toast in role play
* Make 'toast' and 'toppings' in the construction or creative area - write instructions of how to make them.
* Use pastry cutters with dough or clay to make cutouts.
* Continue to offer suitable knives and other implements in the role play and creative areas.
* Make biscuits and discuss how the soft mixture becomes harder when cooked, just like the bread does when toasted.

Stepping Stones and Goals:

Physical development

Yellow - Show awareness of own needs with regard to eating and hygiene

Blue - Show awareness of a range of healthy practices

Green - Show some understanding that good practices can relate to good health

Early Learning Goals - Recognise the importance of keeping healthy and those things those contribute to this

Key Stage One Science:

Sc1 f - explore, using the senses of sight, hearing, smell, touch and taste as appropriate, and make and record observations and measurements

Snack type: Bread

Activity: Quick baking

What you need: part baked bread and rolls

Suggestions - **You can get a wide range of different breads and rolls part baked, ready for you to finish in your oven. Look in a big supermarket for varieties.**

You also need - **plates, round ended knives, soft butter or other spread, oven gloves or cloth, bread board or cutting board, sweet or savoury toppings of your choice**

What you do:

1. Try different breads on different days - just the smell of fresh bread will be enough to get children and adults hungry and interested.
2. Remind children of the safety rules for hot places, things and activities.
3. Put the bread in the oven and use a clock or timer to time the cooking. Children could look at the toppings, or sing some baking songs (eg 5 Brown Buns in the Baker's Shop; Pat a Cake) while they wait.
4. When the bread is cooked, take it out carefully using the oven gloves.
5. Take care when you cut the bread, it will be very hot, even though it has only been in the oven for a short time.
6. Let the bread cool a bit before children spread the pieces of bread themselves. You could talk about the baked bread smell, colour and texture while you wait.
7. Take photos of the bread before and after baking for a 'Before and After' display.

* Always check for gluten allergy or sensitivity before offering grain based food.

Extensions and follow up ideas:

* Encourage them to try things that they have not tried before
* With the children, make a safety notice for your cooking area or activities, including using knives, hot surfaces, washing hands etc.
* Talk about how the bread has changed in the oven. How do other things change as they cook? Take before and after photos (cooked and un-cooked) of eggs, potatoes, pasta, custard, sausages etc.
* Talk about the difference between the foods we eat raw and those we eat cooked - and those we eat both raw <u>and</u> cooked.
* Look at some recipe books of bread cakes and other food. Find a book about baking. Go and watch chickens cooking in a supermarket rotisserie.
* Bring in a bread-making machine and try some recipes.
* Ask a local bakery if you can make a visit.

Stepping Stones and Goals:

Physical development

Yellow - Show awareness of own needs with regard to eating and hygiene

Blue -   Show awareness of a range of healthy practices

Green - Show some understanding that good practices can relate to good health

Early Learning Goals - Recognise the importance of keeping healthy and those things those contribute to this

Key Stage One Science:

Sc1 f - explore, using the senses of sight, hearing, smell, touch and taste as appropriate, and make and record observations and measurements

1a -   study a range of domestic and environmental contexts that are familiar and of interest to them

Snack type: Cakes and biscuits

Activity: Exploring taste

What you need: a range of sweet & savoury biscuits

    Suggestions - look on the wrappers for lower fat and sugar in sweet biscuits, and lower salt in savoury ones

    You also need - plates

What you do:

1. You could have a range of sweet biscuits on the first day, savoury on the next and so on; or you could have sweet and savoury on the same day. Remember that younger children may need a more restricted range, so they don't get too confused. Keep the wrappers for displays and charts.
2. Get the children to help you put the different biscuits on separate plates. You could have different plates for sweet and savoury biscuits.
3. If the biscuits are big, you could break them into pieces. Don't confuse the children into taking the biggest biscuit, rather than the sort they like!
4. Look at the different biscuits, their size, shape and texture.
5. Pass the plates around so everyone can choose which to have. The children could take two pieces from different coloured plates.
6. After tasting the biscuits, talk about the differences between the sorts, using words to describe taste (sweet, spicy, salty), texture (crumbly, hard, crunchy, bumpy) and smell (sugary, sweet, floury, peppery).
7. Stick the wrappers to a big sheet of paper and make a chart by joining names or faces to favourite biscuits.

* Always check for gluten allergy or sensitivity before offering grain based food.

Extensions and follow up ideas:

* Can they guess the flavour from the smell?
* What is the same about the biscuits? What is different?
* Which do they prefer and why?
* Discuss healthy eating, and why we should not eat too many biscuits.
* Older children could look at the ingredients of different biscuits, and make a chart to show which ingredients are the most common.
* Make some sweet or savoury biscuits - cheese straws and shortbread are easy recipes. Make up your own recipes based on those from recipe books.
* Have a biscuit cafe or a coffee morning and invite parents or other children to come. Bake your own biscuits, make tablecloths, decorate table napkins, write invitations.
* Set up a role play café with dough for making biscuits and cakes.
* Make a collection of all the different biscuit wrappers you can find. Write their names in a book with photos of the biscuits or their wrappers.
* Discuss likes and dislikes, talk about how it is fine to have different likes from your friend.

Stepping Stones and Goals:

Knowledge and Understanding of the World: Exploration and investigation

Yellow - Show curiosity

Blue - Describe simple features

Green - Examine objects and living things to find out more about them

Early Learning Goals - Investigate objects by using all of their senses as appropriate

Key Stage One Science:

Sc1 f- explore, using the senses of sight, hearing, smell, touch and taste as appropriate, and make and record observations and measurements

Snack type: **Cakes and biscuits**

Activity: **Flapjacks and cereal bars**

What you need: a range of bars

> Suggestions - some supermarkets now sell packs of small pieces of flapjack, ideal for this activity
>
> You also need - plates, a knife

What you do:

1. Let the children help you put the snacks on plates. You could mix the types or keep one to each plate. Cut the bars and flapjacks into small pieces, so children are not put off or distracted by the size of the pieces.
2. Pass the plates round so everyone can see.
3. If the biscuits are big, you could break them into pieces. Don't confuse the children into taking the biggest biscuit, rather than the sort they like!
4. Look at the different biscuits, their size, shape and texture.
5. Pass the plates around so everyone can choose which to have. The children could take two pieces from different coloured plates.
6. If they can wait, you could discuss the differences and similarities, what the bars are made from, how they smell etc.
7. After tasting the flapjacks and bars, talk about the differences between the sorts, using words to describe taste, texture and smell.
8. Older children could look at the healthy eating diagram on page 7 and talk about the ingredients and where they fit in a healthy diet.

* Always check for gluten and nut allergies before offering these snacks. Children who have a gluten problem may be able to eat nuts, but check first.

54

Extensions and follow up ideas:

* Can they guess the flavour of the bar from the smell?
* Do they know what the biscuits are made from? Which do they prefer, and why?
* Look at the ingredients for different bars and flapjacks. Make a chart to show which ingredients are the most common.
* Make your own flapjacks and cereal bars. They are very easy to make. Make up own mixtures of fruit, oats, seeds and nuts.
* Set up a Health Food Shop - with packets, food, fruit, nuts etc. Make dough flapjack by mixing dough with oats, sand or uncooked rice grains.
* Find out the most popular flapjack/bar in the school or setting.
* Discuss different likes and dislikes, talk about how it is fine to have different likes from your friends.
* Older children could take the bars or flapjacks apart and look at them with magnifying glasses to identify all the listed ingredients that they can find. Compare these ingredients with a recipe - what has disappeared? Where has it gone? Why can't they find it?

Stepping Stones and Goals:

Knowledge and Understanding of the World: Exploration and investigation
Yellow - Show curiosity
Blue - Describe simple features
Green - Examine objects and living things to find out more about them
Early Learning Goals - Investigate objects by using all of their senses as appropriate

Key Stage One Science:

Sc1 f- explore, using the senses of sight, hearing, smell, touch and taste as appropriate, and make and record observations and measurements

Snack type: Cakes and biscuits

Activity: Counting and comparing

What you need: sweet & savoury biscuits with holes

Suggestions - many different biscuits have holes in them. They are put there to stop the biscuits bending during cooking, and so they cook evenly. Look for biscuits with different numbers of holes for this activity. Small biscuits are easier to manage

You also need - plates, card, scissors, felt pens

This activity is more suitable for older children, or at least those who can count!

What you do:

1. Put the different sorts of biscuits on different plates (coloured plates will help with sorting later).
2. Offer the children a choice of two biscuits each.
3. Help the children to count the number of holes in each biscuit. Compare the different sorts of biscuits. Which sort of biscuit has most/least holes?
4. Draw each different type and record the number of holes in each.
5. Now say they can eat the biscuit with the most/least holes.
6. Now make some card replicas of the different sorts of biscuits and help the children to draw the correct number of holes on each. Use the cards for a More/Less game in pairs. Put the cards face down and take turns to take a card. The person with the most holes in their biscuit wins both cards. If the cards are the same, put them back.

* Always check for gluten and nut allergies before offering these snacks.

Extensions and follow up ideas:

* Talk about healthy eating and not to eat too many biscuits.
* Make a role play biscuit factory with dough for biscuits of different types, shapes and sizes. Don't forget cream and chocolate biscuits as well.
* Use opportunities for counting and matching everywhere - How many biscuits do we need for everyone to have one, or two, or three? Have we got enough biscuits on the plate for everyone to have one?
* Make lots of biscuits with play dough. Put different numbers of holes in with a pencil or stick. Bake them hard and use them for games such as Snap or pairs.
* Use the dough biscuits for addition and subtraction, for example taking two (or three) biscuits and adding the holes; taking two and subtracting the larger number from the smaller.
* Print patterns with dots, using Aboriginal art as a stimulus.
* You could do many of these comparing activities with biscuits of different sizes, shapes or thicknesses.

Stepping Stones and Goals:

Knowledge and Understanding of the World: Exploration and investigation

Yellow - Show curiosity

Blue - Describe simple features

Green - Examine objects and living things to find out more about them

Early Learning Goals - Investigate objects by using all of their senses as appropriate.

Mathematical development: Calculating

Early Learning Goals - use language such as more, less, greater, smaller to compare two numbers or quantities; begin to relate addition to combining two groups of objects & subtraction to taking away

Key Stage One Mathematics:

Ma2 2a - count reliably up to 20 objects at first and recognise that if the objects are rearranged the number stays the same

Snack type: **Cakes and biscuits**

Activity: **Exploring shape**

What you need: a range of sweet and savoury
biscuits of different shapes

Suggestions - look on the wrappers for lower fat,
sugar and salt varieties

You also need - plates

What you do:

1. Concentrate on two different shapes at first, till you get an idea of how well they cope with discriminating shape. Remember that younger children may need a more restricted range, so they don't get too confused. Keep the wrappers for displays and charts.

2. Try to find biscuits that are familiar, simple shapes (circles, squares, rectangles, hexagons). More complex shapes will confuse!

3. Get the children to help you put the different biscuits on separate plates. You could have different plates for different shapes, or mix them up.

4. Look at the different biscuits, and talk about the shapes. Use big and small as well as the shapes.

5. Pass the plates around so everyone can choose two biscuits. You could restrict the choice so they choose the same shape, or try different shapes. Try both on different days.

6. Before they eat them (if they can wait!) get each child to say what they have - 'Mine are the same shape, both circles,' or 'Mine are different, one's a square, one's round.'

* Always check for gluten and nut allergies before offering these snacks.

Extensions and follow up ideas:

* Try using rice crackers for a change - these come in squares and circles.
* Offer toppings of different shapes, slices of cucumber, circles cut from cheese slices (use tiny biscuit cutters), triangles of ham etc.
* Collect biscuit wrappers and pictures of different shaped biscuits. Use these to compare biscuits of the same shape, but different sizes.
* Make your own biscuits in different shapes. Use a lower sugar recipe for a healthier option.
* Buy some plain biscuits and give the children icing pens or cheese in tubes to decorate them, following the shape of the biscuit.
* Make dough biscuits in different shapes and sizes, and bake them hard for role play or maths games.
* Use dough shapes to make repeating patterns - square, circle, square, circle; or triangle, circle, triangle, circle.
* Older children could investigate biscuits with more complicated shapes - hexagons, octagons etc. You could help them to replicate these shapes in card and use them for tessellation or matching games.
* Make sponge or potato printing shapes for repeating shape patterns.

Stepping Stones and Goals:

Mathematical development: shape, space, measures

Yellow - Show an interest in shape and space; show awareness of similarities in shapes in the environment

Blue - Begin to talk about the shapes of everyday objects

Green - Show curiosity by talking about shapes, how they are the same, and how different

Early Learning Goals - Use language such as 'circle' and 'bigger' to describe shapes

Key Stage One Maths:

Ma3 2a - describe properties of shapes they can see or visualise using the related vocabulary

Snack type: Cakes and biscuits

Activity: Problem solving

What you need: a variety of small cakes & buns

Suggestions - supermarkets sell boxes of small cakes and buns, muffins and cookies, perfect for this sort of activity

Suggestions - you could also slice swiss rolls or loaf type cakes, or make fairy cakes with the children

What you do:

1. For the youngest children, just solving the problem of which cake to have may be enough! When move gently to the simple 'Are there enough?' questions in pairs and small groups, before posing more difficult problems.

2. Put the cakes on plates so the children can see them. Then give the children a problem to solve. Here are some examples:
   * are there enough cakes?
   * how do we cut the cake so it's fair?
   * how do we cut different shapes so the pieces are fair?
   * what do we do if there are not enough for everyone to have a cake?
   * what happens if we cut the buns in half? Are there enough now? Are there any left over?
   * what happens if someone doesn't want one - how can we make it fair?

3. Older children could do this in groups, each group solving the problem for themselves, then comparing solutions.

* Always check for gluten and nut allergies before offering these snacks.

Extensions and follow up ideas:

* Talk about how cakes are made in a bakery, and how the baker makes sure all the loaves and cakes come out the same size.
* Talk about cakes and bread, and the part they play in a healthy diet.
* Look at the ingredients of the different cakes.
* Try and get some role play food that divides into sections for practice in sharing in your café or house area. (Try Early Learning Centre for food that joins with Velcro and can be shared by pulling or 'cutting' apart)
* Make buns or biscuits and talk about how you make them the same size (using bun tins, paper cases, cutters etc).
* Develop a problem solving approach throughout your room or setting. Give children problems and challenges in maths, technology, craft, outdoor play by asking open questions and giving children opportunities to work things out for themselves, including making mistakes!
* Try making up your own recipes, or giving instructions for making simple things.
* Link problem solving and language by challenging children to think how you could make a cake for a giant or a mouse. Read The Giant Jam Sandwich.

Stepping Stones and Goals:

Mathematical development: problem solving

Yellow - Show an interest in shape and space

Blue - Show an interest in number problems

Green - Sometimes show confidence and offer solutions to problems

Early Learning Goals - Use developing mathematical ideas and methods to solve practical problems

Key Stage One Mathematics:

Ma2 1b - develop flexible approaches to problem solving and look for ways to overcome difficulties

Snack type: Cereal

Activity: What is breakfast cereal made from?

What you need: a variety of breakfast cereals

> Suggestions - There are scores to choose from, but it would be healthier to avoid the sugar coated ones! Over time, try to offer cereals made from wheat, oats, corn, rice, and other grains and seeds
>
> You also need - small bowls/clean yogurt pots/margarine tubs/polystyrene pots, spoons, milk in small jugs

What you do:

1. Start by offering two different cereals. Choose ones that look and taste very different, and put a quantity in two larger bowls for the children to help themselves with a spoon.
2. Each child needs two small containers for the two cereals. They can spoon a little of each into each bowl and look for similarities and differences.
3. Now let them try the cereal dry, before offering small jugs of milk.
4. Look at what happens when the milk is added. Talk about floating, sinking, soaking in, getting bigger, dissolving.
5. Make a chart over several days of their likes and dislikes - remember it's alright to like more than one thing, and alright not to like something after you have tried it.
6. Draw some cereal bowls and stick samples of the cereals inside to make your chart. Children can write their name then join it to their favourites.

* Always check for gluten and nut allergies before offering these snacks.

Extensions and follow up ideas:

* Ask the children what they think each cereal is made from. Discuss the different sorts and read the ingredients on the boxes.
* Talk about healthy eating and where cereals fit in a healthy diet.
* Look in books and on the Internet for pictures of the crops before they are cut. There are also lots of entries and sites promoting healthy cereals and what to look for in the dangers.
* Try growing some cereal crops in your setting or school - rice, wheat, maize/sweet corn will all sprout, although they won't grow from the seeds in cereal packets because they have often been cooked, and will always be sterilised. You could try growing bird seed, or ask a garden centre or friendly farmer for some untreated seeds.
* Find out about cereals that grow in this country. Look out for wheat, sweet corn, barley and other crops growing and being harvested. If you live in a city, look for sweet corn on the market or try visiting local allotments.
* Talk abut cereals that are produced in other parts of the world - rice, rye etc. How are they grown and harvested? How do they get to our shops?
* Older children could look at cereal packets and design their own.

Stepping Stones and Goals:

Knowledge and Understanding of the World: Exploration and investigation

Yellow - Show an interest in the world in which they live

Blue - Comment and ask questions about the natural world

Early Learning Goals - Find out about their environment; begin to know about their own culture and those of other people

Key Stage One Science:

Sc1 f - explore, using the senses of sight, hearing, smell, touch and taste as appropriate, and make and record observations and measurements

Snack type: Cereal

Activity: Muesli investigation

What you need: a variety of muesli

Suggestions - balance your choice between
    muesli recipes with high sugar, and those
    with less sugar and more dried fruit,
    crunchy mixtures and smoother ones
You also need - small plates or clean pieces of paper,
    spoons, milk in small jugs

What you do:

1. Start by offering two different cereals. Choose ones that look and taste very different, you can widen the range later. Put a quantity in two larger bowls for the children to help themselves with a spoon.
2. Every child needs a plate to put the muesli on. They can spoon a little of each sort onto their plate and look for similarities and differences.
3. Encourage them to look closely at the different mueslis, separating them out so they can see the ingredients. Talk about what you find. Do they know the names of the ingredients? Older children can look on the packet and see how many of the ingredients they can see. What has happened to the ones they can't see?
4. After your muesli investigation, try some, with or without milk.

* Check for gluten and nut allergies

Extensions and follow up ideas:

* Make a chart of all the ingredients, to show what they found the most of, least of, which ingredients are on the packet that they could not find.
* Design and make your own own muesli. Buy the ingredients separately at a health food shop and put them in separate bowls. The children can then make the mixture they like by taking spoonfuls of the different ingredients.
* Take photos of the separate ingredients and make a photo book of We Can Make Muesli.
* Discuss healthy eating, how important it is to eat breakfast, and that cereal helps their brain to work. Encourage children (and parents) to eat cereals with lower salt and sugar levels.
* Get some leaflets about breakfasts and offer them to parents. Remind them that in winter, children need high energy food, and cereals have a 'slow burn', releasing energy throughout the morning.

Stepping Stones and Goals:

Knowledge and Understanding of the World: Exploration and investigation

Yellow - Describe simple features

Blue - Describe simple features of objects and events

Green - Examine objects and living things to find out more about them

Early Learning Goals - Investigate objects by using all of their senses as appropriate

Key Stage One Science:

Sc1 f - explore, using the senses of sight, hearing, smell, touch and taste as appropriate, and make and record observations and measurements

Snack type: Rice, pizza, pasta, corn, noodles

Activity: Rice

What you need: different rices, dry & cooked

> Suggestions - look in your supermarket and in
> Asian shops for different kinds - brown,
> Basmati, risotto, pudding, wild; you
> need some cooked rice for the children to
> try too, and you could get some rice pudding

> You also need - small bowls/clean yogurt pots/margarine
> tubs/polystyrene pots, spoons; you could also add Indian and Chinese
> sauces to pour over

What you do:

1. Cook some of the rice before you start.
2. Now tip different kinds of dry rice into different bowls. Pass the bowls round and talk about the different size, types and colours of the grains.
3. Talk about rice and how it fills you up and gives you energy. Talk about the way some people like potatoes best, some like bread, some like noodles or pasta, and some like rice. People who live in India, China and other Asian countries often eat rice because it grows in their countries. In the UK we eat a lot of potatoes because they grow here. You could also say that we eat all these things to make us strong and healthy.
4. Talk about all the different sorts of food we eat - Chinese, Indian, Italian, French - each of these has its special starchy foods, but in the UK we now like to be able to eat all of them!
5. Now try some of the cooked rice - the plain cooked rice, some with sauces added and some of the rice pudding. Ask the children which they like best.

* Always check for gluten and nut allergies before offering these snacks.

Extensions and follow up ideas:

* Offer the children some chopsticks to try. You can now buy chopsticks fixed at one end which makes it easier to manage. If you or one of the children can eat with chopsticks, give a demonstration.
* Compare rice fields with local fields in the UK.
* Provide books, music, songs, stories and pictures about India and China.
* Do some experiments with other dried cereals, such as tabbouleh or bulgar wheat, which can be eaten without further cooking. Make these into salads by adding chopped tomato, cucumber and sweet corn.
* Try semolina, tapioca or rice pudding with jam or honey.
* Make a rice farm in your water tray.
* Have a role play Chinese take away or an Indian restaurant.
* Make dry coloured rice in trays to explore (put some dry rice in a cup, add a couple of drops of food colouring and stir. It will take the colour but remain dry). Put the dry coloured rice in creative area, to make pictures, patterns etc.

Stepping Stones and Goals:

Physical development

Yellow - Show awareness of own needs with regard to eating and hygiene

Blue - Show awareness of a range of healthy practices

Green - Show some understanding that good practices can relate to good health

Early Learning Goals - Recognise the importance of keeping healthy and those things which contribute to this.

Key Stage One Geography:

3e - recognise how places are linked to other places in the world e.g. Food from other countries

Snack type: Rice, pizza, pasta, corn & noodles

Activity: Pasta

What you need: different types of pasta

> Suggestions - look in your supermarket for different kinds - spaghetti, macaroni, pasta shapes, lasagne sheets, stars, letters, shells etc - a different one for each day of the week
>
> You also need - pans for cooking, small bowls or polystyrene pots, pasta sauce in small bowls, spoons, forks

What you do:

1. Look at some dry pasta shapes first. Talk about how they might be made, what they are made from, how they get soft enough to eat.
2. Now show the children how pasta is cooked by boiling it in water. Make sure they know the safety rules for hot food and objects.
3. Remind children that eating pasta, potatoes and rice are all good for them.
4. Give each child some pasta, or put it where they can help themselves. Let them add sauces to their little cup of pasta before trying it. Younger children will do best if you let them use their fingers to dip pasta pieces into the sauce. There will be drips and spills!
5. Talk about texture and taste and preference.
6. Remind children that tasting is the important bit, not eating every bit.

n.b. If you can't cook the pasta in your setting or school, cook it at home and add a little oil to stop it sticking together. Then have cold pasta salad instead of hot pasta with sauce.

* Always check for gluten and nut allergies before offering these snacks.

Extensions and follow up ideas:

* Put piles of dry pasta in trays to explore pouring, filling, emptying, sorting.
* Offer dry pasta in the creative area, to make pictures and patterns or to press into dough.
* Put saucepans and spoons with dry pasta in the home corner for imaginative domestic play.
* Use pasta for counting, sharing etc
* Turn your role play area into an Italian Restaurant, serving pasta, pizza and ice cream.
* Find out about Italy/Italian people through pictures, video, books and the internet.

Stepping Stones and Goals:

Physical development

Yellow - Show awareness of own needs with regard to eating and hygiene

Blue - Show awareness of a range of healthy practices

Green - Show some understanding that good practices can relate to good health

Early Learning Goals - Recognise the importance of keeping healthy and those things which contribute to this.

Knowledge and understanding of the world

Yellow - Show an interest in the world in which they live

Blue - Comment and ask questions about the natural world

Green - Gain an awareness of the cultures of others

Early Learning Goals - Find out about their environment; begin to know about their own culture and those of other people

Key Stage One Geography:

3e - recognise how places are linked to other places in the world e.g. Food from other countries

Snack type: Rice, pizza, pasta, corn, noodles

Activity: Noodles

What you need: packets of noodles

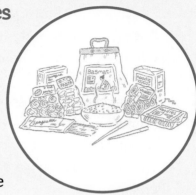

> Suggestions - noodles are great for snacks, because they are easy to prepare, and most children like them
>
> You also need - Japanese and other sauces, small bowls, spoons, forks, chopsticks, a kettle and two large bowls

What you do:

1. Look at the dry noodles and pass a few round for the children to feel.
2. Now put the noodles in big bowls and cover with very hot water (remember the safety rules).
3. Watch the noodles as they cook, talking about how they change in look and texture. Stir them with a fork as they cook, so the children can see how they change.
4. Give each child some of the noodles (two sorts if you can get them).
5. Offer the children sauces in small bowls, so they can choose a sauce and spoon a little over their noodles.
6. Give a choice of spoons, forks or chopsticks for eating the noodles.
7. Talk about flavours and texture of the noodles, as they taste each sort.
8. Have different noodles on different days.

* Always check for gluten and nut allergies before offering these snacks.

Extensions and follow up ideas:

* Look at a map of the world to find Japan. Look at pictures and books about Japan
* Look on the internet for pictures and information about Japan.
* Put chopsticks, woks etc in the role play area. You could add some cooked noodles r some lengths of wool and string to practice using chopsticks.
* Have a Japanese restaurant role play. Make menus, posters and price lists. Older children may like to look at Japanese writing, compare this with other character alphabets.
* Provide opportunities to experiment with noodles- put noodles in cold water and watch what happens.
* Use cooked noodles to make pictures and patterns on black paper without glue. Cook the noodles, arrange them on the paper and leave to dry - they will stick with their own starch.

Stepping Stones and Goals:
Physical development
Yellow - Show awareness of own needs with regard to eating and hygiene
Blue -   Show awareness of a range of healthy practices
Green - Show some understanding that good practices can relate to good health
Early Learning Goals - Recognise the importance of keeping healthy and those things which contribute to this.

Key Stage One Geography:
3e -   recognise how places are linked to other places in the world e.g. Food from other countries

Snack type: Rice, pizza, pasta, corn, noodles

Activity: Tortillas & Taco Shells (or corn chips)

What you need: Flour tortillas, taco shells, tortilla chips

    Suggestions - Try to get some different sorts from a big supermarket (both come in lots of flavours)

    You also need - small bowls for dips and fillings (pate, cheese, chopped tomatoes, cold meat, thin slices of fruit and vegetables, sausages, sweet corn, baked beans, Mexican sauces or mild salsa etc), suitable knives and boards

What you do:

1. Put the taco shells and tortillas in baskets or on plates and pass them round. Younger children might manage better with chips rather than taco shells.
2. Encourage the children to talk together about colour, texture and smell of Mexican food. Older children may want to talk about where Mexico is.
3. Now let the children prepare the fillings, chopping, slicing, mixing, pouring into bowls. Talk about the texture, smell and colour of the fillings.
4. Make sure you tell children which of the fillings are spicy! Encourage them to taste a little on a spoon or chip before filling a taco or tortilla with it.
5. Cut the tortillas into four to make them more manageable, and show the children how to fill and roll them.
6. Now let the children choose their fillings for a tortilla or taco snack.

* Always check for gluten and nut allergies before offering these snacks.

Extensions and follow up ideas:

* Talk about 'spiciness'. Think of all the different foods we now eat and where they are from. Use a globe or world map to look for the countries.
* Find some books about other countries and see if you can find information about Mexico, India, China etc.
* Talk about the foods children eat at home, celebrating diversity. Talk about takeaways, restaurants and foods cooked at home. Remind older children about the foods we cook from other countries, which have become familiar standards - spaghetti, rice, pizzas, chilli.
* Have a role play Taco Bar with tacos, tortillas and fillings made from recycled materials.
* Look on the Internet for pictures and information about Mexico.
* Talk about healthy eating, trying new things and eating a varied diet.

Stepping Stones and Goals:

Physical development
Yellow - Show awareness of own needs with regard to eating and hygiene
Blue - Show awareness of a range of healthy practices
Green - Show some understanding that good practices can relate to good health
Early Learning Goals - Recognise the importance of keeping healthy and those things which contribute to this.

Knowledge and understanding of the world
Yellow - Show an interest in the world in which they live
Blue - Comment and ask questions about the natural world
Green - Gain an awareness of the cultures of others
Early Learning Goals - Find out about their environment; begin to know about their own culture and those of other people

Key Stage One Geography:

3e - recognise how places are linked to other places in the world e.g. food from other countries

Key Stage One Science:

Sc1 f - explore, using the senses of sight, hearing, smell, touch and taste as appropriate, and make and record observations and measurements

Snack type: Rice, pizza, pasta, corn & noodles
Activity: Pizza
What you need:

- French bread or mini pizza bases
- tomato puree for spreading on bases
- toppings, either raw or cooked
- grated cheese

You also need:

- small bowls/clean yogurt pots/margarine tubs/
  polystyrene pots, spoons; a grill or oven

What you do:

1. Let the children help to prepare the toppings, grate the cheese, chop tomatoes, peppers, mushrooms etc. and put them in small bowls.
2. Talk about the different toppings - how they look and smell. Discuss favourites and favourite combinations.
3. Now look at the pizza bases you have chosen.
4. Show the children how to spread tomato sauce on the base and sprinkle other ingredients over the top before adding some grated cheese.
5. Now let each child construct their own pizza, helping them if they need it. Don't make any assumptions about combinations! Some children are very adventurous, some are very cautious.
6. Grill or bake the pizzas until the cheese is golden.
7. Make sure the pizzas have time to cool before the children eat them - melted cheese gets very hot.

* Always check for gluten and nut allergies before offering these snacks.

Extensions and follow up ideas:

* Have a 'Pizza Hut' in Role play, make the pizzas, take photos, make a menu.
* Have a pizza delivery service, adapt a trike, make delivery boxes with the telephone number on the side, give the driver a mobile phone and clipboard,
* Find out about Italy/ Italian people through pictures, books and the internet
* Explore pizza boxes by unfolding them to see how they are made.
* Make the Leaning Tower of Pizza from empty pizza boxes!!
* Explore simple fractions by cutting pizza-shapes pieces of card in different ways.
* Cut circles of card into different numbers of pieces for different numbers of people, exploring division.
* Make a pizza shaped 'pie chart' to show preferences of toppings.
* Make pretend pizza collages with collage bits and recycled materials (a garlic press makes good grated cheese from dough).
* For a special treat, order a take-away pizza to be delivered at your setting.

Stepping Stones and Goals:

Physical development
Yellow - Show awareness of own needs with regard to eating and hygiene
Blue -   Show awareness of a range of healthy practices
Green - Show some understanding that good practices can relate to good health
Early Learning Goals - Recognise the importance of keeping healthy and those things
            which contribute to this.
Knowledge and understanding of the world
Yellow - Show an interest in the world in which they live
Blue -   Comment and ask questions about the natural world
Green - Gain an awareness of the cultures of others
Early Learning Goals - Find out about their environment; begin to know about their own
            culture and those of other people

Key Stage One Geography:

3e -   recognise how places are linked to other places in the world e.g. by eating food
            from other countries

Snack type: Rice, pizza, pasta, corn & noodles

Activity: Party snacks

What you need:

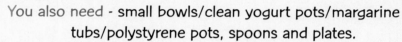

>   Suggestions - different types and kinds of small, party sized snacks (eg samosas, onion bajis, spring rolls, cheese and sausage rolls, sushi etc); you could also add some dips

>   You also need - small bowls/clean yogurt pots/margarine tubs/polystyrene pots, spoons and plates.

What you do:

1. Let the children help to put the different snacks on plates.
2. Pass them round and look at them, talk about the different sorts, shapes, smells and ingredients. For younger children, who may not have eaten these things before, you could cut some of the snacks into smaller pieces, then they can see what is inside, and try a smaller piece. Make sure the children know the names of the different snacks.
3. Think and talk about the different countries and communities the snacks are from. Older children may like to find the countries on a map or globe. Encourage children to talk about the snacks they have already tasted.
4. Now pass the plates round so each child can choose something to taste. Encourage them to try, but don't insist on eating everything - a little nibble is enough. Have some cups of water on hand, as they try something else.
5. Talk about tastes and flavours, and which they like best.

* Always check for gluten and nut allergies before offering these snacks.

Extensions and follow up ideas:

* Look at the snack wrappings and talk about the different ingredients used in each snack. Carefully explore a small piece of each snack with a magnifying glass to see if you can find the ingredients.
* Talk about the different spices and ingredients used, show the children some dried and fresh herbs and spices, such as coriander, bean sprouts, cumin, garlic, garam masala. Let them smell the different ingredients.
* Grow some beansprouts in a jar (you need mung beans) and make your own spring rolls, or make little vegetable samosas by wrapping a teaspoon of cooked and spiced vegetables in a triangle of pastry and baking or frying them.
* If you work in a mixed race community. ask parents to come and talk about the food they like, or to demonstrate how to make samosas, spring rolls or bajis. You could also make sausage rolls or vol-au-vents with different fillings.
* Go and look at local restaurants and talk-aways to see what sort of foods they serve. Collect recipes, menus, carrier bags etc. for a role play restaurant.
* Use dough or clay in the home corner to make a range of pretend snacks from different countries.

Stepping Stones and Goals:

Physical development

Yellow - Show awareness of own needs with regard to eating and hygiene

Blue -   Show awareness of a range of healthy practices

Green - Show some understanding that good practices can relate to good health

Early Learning Goals - Recognise the importance of keeping healthy and those things which contribute to this

Key Stage One Geography:

3e -   recognise how places are linked to other places in the world e.g. through food from other countries

Snack type: Rice, pizza, pasta, corn & noodles
Activity: Popcorn
What you need:

Suggestions - look for packs of popping corn in a big supermarket - some corn needs a <u>saucepan</u> for cooking, but you can get <u>microwaveable</u> bags too; look on the packet for equipment needed and instructions

You also need - a small amount of melted butter, a sprinkling of salt, or some sugar; small bowls/clean yogurt pots/margarine tubs/polystyrene pots, spoons

What you do:

1. Look at the corn (a specially hard variety of maize which pops when heated) before you cook it. Ask the children if they know what happens when you make popcorn.
2. Now cook the popcorn according to the instructions on the packet. If you are using a saucepan, you will be able to hear the corn 'popping'; if it is in the microwave, listen and watch what happens.
3. Tip the popcorn into a big bowl and talk about what has happened to the corn now it as popped. How does it look and smell?
4. Now add the melted butter and a little salt OR a small amount of sugar. you could do some of each for a taste comparison.
5. Pass the bowl around and try some. Don't force children to try it, more reluctant ones may well be encouraged by others' enjoyment.
6. Talk about the texture, flavour and smell of the popcorn. Choose a favourite - sweet or salty?

* Always check for gluten and nut allergies before offering these snacks.

Extensions and follow up ideas:

* Make up a dance inspired by the popcorn popping in the pan or oven.
* Compare popcorn with other 'popped' cereals - puffed wheat, Sugar Puffs, Rice Crispies, rice cakes.
* Find out about how and where corn/maize grows. Talk about the different ways corn is used - corn on the cob, sweet corn, fresh, tinned and frozen, cornflour, tacos and corn chips, popcorn.
* Try to get some corn on the cob with the leaves still on. Explore unwrapping the corn cob, looking at the silky threads protecting the corn kernels and finally uncovering the yellow kernels themselves. Look at the patterns of kernels in the corn head, count the kernels, look at the way they get smaller as you go up the cob.
* Make Gloop with cornflour and water and play with this strange mixture in a tray or bowl.
* If you have a garden, plant some sweet corn and watch it grow. It will grow far taller than the children.
* Talk about sugary foods and the importance of just having a small amount of these.

Stepping Stones and Goals:

Physical development

Yellow - Show awareness of own needs with regard to eating and hygiene

Blue - Show awareness of a range of healthy practices

Green - Show some understanding that good practices can relate to good health

Early Learning Goals - Recognise the importance of keeping healthy and those things which contribute to this

Key Stage One Science:

Sc1 f - explore, using the senses of sight, hearing, smell, touch and taste as appropriate, and make and record observations and measurements

Snack type: Cheese, dairy, eggs

Activity: Cheese

What you need: try different cheeses every day for a week

Suggestions - at least two types each day (try to get a variety of different cheeses, hard and soft, sharp and mellow, spreading and block, English and from other countries), cheese biscuits or small pieces of bread, apple slices, grapes (optional)

You also need - small plates, safe spreading/cutting knives, boards

What you do:

1. You can offer the cheese in cubed, grated, sliced or spread forms.
2. Let the children see the cheese as you unwrap it, and watch or help grate or cut it for serving.
3. Talk about the different sorts of cheese, and the ones the children prefer.
4. Put the cheeses on plates or in bowls, and put out some small cheese biscuits or pieces of bread. You can also offer fruit if you wish.
5. Encourage the children to pass the food around and take a selection each, spreading or placing the cheese on the biscuits, or eating the cheese on its own. When they have tried one or two sorts, talk about the different flavours and textures, using vocabulary such as sharp, smooth, creamy, soft, crumbly.
6. Try different cheeses on different days, so children get used to trying new flavours and textures.
7. Record likes and dislikes over the week or several days, then try to offer a wide range on the last day, so children can remember.

* Always check for dairy allergies before offering these snacks.

Extensions and follow up ideas:

* Talk about the place of cheese in a healthy diet, using a food pyramid or the food plate on page 7.
* Take photos of the different sorts of cheese to help children choose favourites and remember what they like.
* Find some books or internet sites about how cheese is made. Don't forget that cheese can be made from the milk of goats, sheep, buffalos as well as cows.
* Make some butter or soft cheeses from full cream milk.
* Make cheese on toast, cheese scones or cheese straws.
* Go on a visit to a supermarket so the children can see how many cheeses there are to choose from. If you can't take the children, ask the supermarket if you can take some photos to show them.
* Use a map or globe to identify where cheeses come from.
* Make a cheese recipe book or scrapbook from magazine photos and recipes. Ask parents to contribute cheese recipes. You could even publish it (illustrated by the children) to raise funds for your school or setting!

Stepping Stones and Goals:

Knowledge and Understanding of the world

Yellow - Show curiosity

Blue - Describe simple features

Green - Examine objects and living things to find out more about them

Early Learning Goals - Investigate objects by using all of their senses as appropriate

Key Stage One Science:

Sc1 f - explore, using the senses of sight, hearing, smell, touch and taste as appropriate, and make and record observations and measurements

Snack type: Cheese, dairy, eggs

Activity: Milk and yogurt

What you need: make smoothies & try yogurts

Suggestions - children should drink milk every day; many don't, so tempting them with fruit shakes, smoothies and fruit yogurt may help to increase their calcium intake for healthy bones and teeth

You need - whole milk, berries, bananas and other soft fruit, plastic tumblers, small bowls, a liquidiser, a sieve

What you do:

1. Talk together about milk and how it helps to build strong bones and bodies.
2. Look at some plain yogurt (many children have only tasted sweetened fruit yogurt, so this may be new).
3. Let the children watch as you put milk and berries in the liquidiser. Talk about what happens to the colour and texture of the milk.
4. Give each child a little to try. Talk about the flavour and texture.
5. Now experiment with different fruits. Banana will make the shake thicker, berries will give colour.
6. Talk about the yogurt and try giving the children a little in a plastic cup to taste. Now offer them chopped fruits to add to their yogurt. Stir them in and see how the colour changes. Try different combinations. You could sweeten yogurt or drinks with a little brown sugar or honey.
7. Record likes and dislikes over the week or several days, then try to offer a wide range on the last day, so children can remember.

What's the difference? Milk shakes are made from milk, ice cream and fruit syrup; smoothies are made from milk, yogurt and fruit.

Extensions and follow up ideas:

* Experiment with shakes, smoothies and yogurt mixtures, sweetening them if necessary with honey.
* Take photos of different sorts and make a menu for a Smoothie Bar, with tall plastic glasses and thick straws; or make a poster for healthy drinks.
* Find some books or internet sites about how cheese is made. Don't forget that cheese can be made from the milk of goats, sheep, buffalos as well as cows.
* Compare ready made fruit yogurt or smoothies with ones the children make.
* Offer fruit slices with yogurt dipping sauce, try frozen yogurt.

Blueberry Pineapple Smoothie
* 2 cups chilled fresh or frozen blueberries, slightly thawed
* 1 cup chilled pineapple-orange juice, or pineapple-orange-strawberry juice
* 1 8 oz. carton vanilla nonfat yogurt
* 1 tablespoon sugar

Combine all ingredients in a blender and puree until smooth.

Banana Strawberry Fruit Smoothie
* 1 banana, frozen
* 6 strawberries, frozen
* 1 1/4 cup water
* 1 tbsp. skim milk powder

Combine all ingredients in a blender and puree until smooth.

Stepping Stones and Goals:
Knowledge and Understanding of the world

Yellow - Show curiosity

Blue - Talk about what is seen and what is happening

Green - Show an awareness of change

Early Learning Goals - Ask questions about why things happen and how things work

Key Stage One Science:
Sc1 f - explore, using the senses of sight, hearing, smell, touch and taste as appropriate, and make and record observations and measurements

Safety advice on using eggs: The risk of getting salmonella from eggs is partly in touching the shells if they haven't been pasteurised. The advice to nurseries and schools is that you should use pasteurised eggs (whole or separated); these are available in most supermarkets. You should also make sure that eggs are well cooked before children eat them. Boiled eggs must be cooked so the white and the yolk are firm. Young children should NOT eat soft boiled eggs! However, hard boiled eggs are quite safe for children to eat, and to use in any recipe using cooked eggs.

Snack type: Cheese, dairy, eggs
Activity: Eggs

What you need: eggs

      You also need - bread, crackers, butter or soft spread

                    - cooking utensils, small plates, safe spreading/cutting knives, boards

What you do:

1. Decide which sort of eggs you will cook. Scrambled eggs are an easy way if you want to explore the change when eggs are cooked. Hard boiled eggs are straightforward and can be chopped or sliced to see the different parts. Omelettes are good for sharing and can be filled with a variety of things.
2. If you are using pasteurised eggs, the children can handle them carefully to see how they feel.
3. Talk about the egg shapes and colours, and where they come from. Break an egg into a bowl and pass it round for the children to look at.
4. Cook the eggs in the way you decide eg boiling in a pan, scrambling in a microwave.
5. Try the eggs in different ways on different days.

REMEMBER - PASTEURISED EGGS ARE SAFER

Extensions and follow up ideas:

* Make clay or plaster eggs to decorate. Have an egg hunt. (Don't use real eggs for Egg Hunts, they may get dirty).
* Look for stories, fact books, videos about eggs, chicks and birds. Try 'Horton Hatches the Egg', 'Are you my Mother?', 'Chicken Licken', 'The Hungry Caterpillar', 'The Chicken That Wouldn't Hatch', 'Green Eggs and Ham', 'Hens in the Garden', 'Dora's Eggs'. Try a search on the Internet for information about eggs.
* Make up a hatching dance and use percussion instruments to make a musical accompaniment.
* Try some different sorts of eggs - quail, duck, goose, ostrich.
* Look at bird books.
* Look for egg recipes and make a recipe book. Take photos of different sorts of eggs and add them to the book. Try the internet for recipes and craft ideas.
* Hire an incubator and hatch some eggs, or get a butterfly farm and hatch your own butterflies.

Stepping Stones and Goals:

Knowledge and Understanding of the world

Yellow - Show curiosity

Blue - Describe simple features

Green - Examine objects and living things to find out more about them

Early Learning Goals - Investigate objects by using all of their senses as appropriate

Key Stage One Science

Sc1 f - explore, using the senses of sight, hearing, smell, touch and taste as appropriate, and make and record observations and measurements

Snack type: Cheese, dairy, eggs
Activity: Dips
What you need: a variety of dairy based dips

Suggestions - get a variety of dairy based dips (yogurt and cheese) and compare two types each day over a few days or a week; then have them all available on the last day to choose absolute favourites; try tsatsiki, cottage cheese, cheese & chive, salmon, spicy Asian dips; vegetables to cut into sticks and slices

You also need - small plates, bowls, safe spreading/cutting knives, boards

What you do:

1. Get the children to help wash and cut vegetables and fruit into sticks (apple, celery, carrot, pepper, courgette, mushroom, cucumber).
2. Look at the different dips you have brought, talk about flavours, colours, smells and textures. tell the children what is in each dip, so they can make informed choices.
3. Pass the food sticks round so children can take a few each. Remind them not to put a stick back in the dip after they have licked it!
4. Discuss flavours and textures and combinations of stick and dip.
5. Encourage the children to try as many combinations as they like and choose favourites for the day. Make a chart by laminating a sheet of photos of the dips, then children can mark or write their name by their favourite of the day. Then, particularly for older children, you could have all the choices displayed with all the dips on the last day for a final selection.

Extensions and follow up ideas:

* Make your own dips by mixing plain yogurt, cottage cheese or other soft cheese with chopped vegetables, spices, tomato paste, garlic, herbs (dried, chopped fresh herbs or the herbs you can buy in tubes). You can also mix canned fish (salmon, tuna, anchovies etc) with soft cheese for dipping or spreading on crackers.
* Take photos of the stages of the children making and eating dips, to use books and sequencing activities.
* Buy a yogurt making machine and make some of your own yogurt, or make a simple soft cheese (recipe at the end of the book).
* Look at the ingredients on the dip pots and find out what they are. Why does shop dip have extra ingredients?
* Make a cheesecake (look on the internet for simple recipes specially written for children).
* Visit your local supermarket and see how many different dips you can find, or use an internet shopping service to compare prices and varieties.

Stepping Stones and Goals:

Physical development

Yellow - Show awareness of own needs with regard to eating and hygiene

Blue - Show awareness of a range of healthy practices

Green - Show some understanding that good practices can relate to good health

Early Learning Goals - Recognise the importance of keeping healthy and those things which contribute to this

Key Stage One Science:

Sc2 2c - that taking exercise and eating the right types and amounts of food help humans to keep healthy

Snack type: Cheese, dairy, eggs

Activity: Pancakes

What you need: flour, milk, eggs

Pancake recipe - 125g self raising flour

- 1 egg
- 300ml milk; a pinch of salt

You also need - a mixing bowl, fish slice or palette knife, a small strong frying pan, small plates, safe spreading knives, spoons

Fillings - eg honey, fruit spread, cream cheese, hummus, lemon and sugar

What you do:

1. Let the children help you to make the mixture. Measure out the flour and add a pinch of salt. Make a well in the middle of the flour and break in the egg. Add the milk and gradually mix the flour into the egg and milk mixture. Beat well with a wooden spoon or whisk. Leave for a few minutes before cooking.
2. Heat the pan and add a very small amount of oil or butter (adult only!).
3. Carefully spoon some pancake mixture into the pan and cook till it just starts to solidify round the edges. Flip or toss the pancake over. When it is cooked, lift out onto a plate. Cool before spreading and eating.
4. While you are waiting, talk about how the pancake batter changes as it cooks.
5. Let the children choose and spread their own fillings from small bowls. They can either cut the pancakes up or roll them to eat them.

Safety tip: if you are cooking on a stove, remember to keep the children safely away from the hot surfaces, preferably behind a barrier of some sort. Remind them frequently that things may still be hot, even thought they don't look hot! When working with younger children make sure you have extra adults and keep the groups small.

Extensions and follow up ideas:

* Make different shaped pancakes by putting metal cookie cutters in the pan before pouring in the batter. Then the children can choose the shape they like.
* Talk about likes and dislikes, practice and use 'sweet' and 'savoury'.
* Read the Great Big Enormous Pancake story and act it out.
* Make some pretend pancakes and have a pancake race.
* Explain to older children the origins of Pancake Day, how people made pancakes to use up flour, milk and butter before Lent.
* Many countries have pancakes, they are made from a range of ingredients and called different names. Find out about (and try making) different sorts of pancakes around the world - Scotch pancakes, American pancakes, tortillas, French crepes, blintzes, potato pancakes etc. You could make a cookery book of all the different sorts. Ask parents for ideas for fillings and have a chart to show what people have tried and liked.
* Take photos of the way to make pancakes or of your own version of the Enormous Pancake story.

Stepping Stones and Goals:

Mathematical development

Yellow - Show an interest in counting

Blue -   begin to talk about the shapes of everyday objects

Green -   Count, saying one number for each item up to 6; order items by size

Early Learning Goals - Use language such as circle, or bigger to describe the shape and size of solids

Key Stage One Maths:

Ma3 2a - describe properties of shapes they can see or visualise using the related vocabulary

Snack type: Nuts and seeds

Activity: Raw and roasted nuts and seeds

What you need: a variety of nuts and seeds

> Suggestions - scour your supermarket and health shops for different nuts and seeds, raw and toasted (try to avoid the very salty ones) eg cashews, sunflower seeds, pumpkin seeds, pistachios, peanuts, sesame, almonds, walnuts; try to find some nuts still in their shells.

> You also need - small bowls, nutcrackers

What you do:

1. Let the children help to tip the different nuts into separate bowls.
2. Pass the bowls around and look at the different sorts of seeds and nuts. Talk about nuts and seeds and how they are different (nuts have a hard coating to protect the seed inside). If you have some whole nuts, crack some and look at the seeds inside.
3. Now try tasting some of the nuts and seeds. Remind the children that they can only eat the proper sorts of seeds and nuts, or they will be ill. Train them to always ask an adult before eating seeds, nuts or fruit they find in gardens or on walks.
4. Now talk about the foods that are made from seeds and nuts.
5. Buy a few nut and seed bars or Granola type bars and cut them into small pieces for taste tests.

* Safety tip: Remember to check for nut allergies.

Extensions and follow up ideas:

* Make some Trail Bars, Granola Bars or Muesli bars (recipe at end of book, or put Granola Bar recipe in a search engine).
* Find out where the different nuts come from
* Crack open and draw the nuts inside, or take 'inside and outside' photos.
* Use seeds in collages and pictures
* Make a secret message nut tree, the children write messages/ promises/ wishes then put them inside a home made made 'nut' and hang on twigs/ small branches etc. If you carefully crack open walnut shells, you can stick the two halves together again, trapping a piece of silver or gold string to make unique decorations for Christmas or Easter.
* Make bird cake for winter bird feeding - mix bird seed and melted fat and press into containers. Leave till cold then tip out for a tasty treat for cold and hungry birds.
* Try planting some seeds or nuts and watching to see them grow.
* Take an autumn walk to find seeds and nuts in the hedges and fields. Remind the children that some seeds must not be eaten as they will make humans ill.

Stepping Stones and Goals:
Knowledge and Understanding of the world
Yellow - Show curiosity
Blue - Describe simple features
Green - Examine objects and living things to find out more about them
Early Learning Goals - Investigate objects by using all of their senses as appropriate

Key Stage One Science:
Sc1 f- explore, using the senses of sight, hearing, smell, touch and taste as appropriate, and make and record observations and measurements

Snack type: Nuts and seeds

Activity: Sprouts and shoots

What you need: seeds that sprout quickly
and easily indoors

Suggestions - try some of these: alfalfa, mung
(beansprouts), mustard, cress, lentil;
these all produce sprouts that you can eat

You also need - a large plastic or glass jar, colander or sieve

What you do:

1. First, thoroughly rinse about 1/4 cup of larger seeds or 2 tablespoons small seeds or 1/2 cup lentils in a strainer/colander with holes small enough so that the seeds won't fall through. If this is a problem, line the strainer or colander with cloth before you put the beans or seeds in.

2. Place the rinsed beans or seeds in a large clean jar. This will serve as your sprouter. Cover the sprouter opening with cheesecloth or a clean (unused) nylon stocking and secure with a rubber band. <u>Keep the cover on the sprouter through the sprouting process</u>. Fill the jar with lukewarm water, and let it soak at room temperature overnight.

3. The next day, pour off the water, then gently rinse and drain again.

4. Place the jar on a tilt in a warm, dark place. This lets moisture out and oxygen in. In about 3 to 5 days, the beans or seeds will sprout. Rinse every day.

5. When the sprouts reach the same length as their original bean, pea or seed, place the jar in a sunny spot so the sprouts will turn green. Rinse the sprouts and drain well before storing in the refrigerator. The sprouts will keep up to two weeks if tightly sealed in a plastic bag or jar.

Extensions and follow up ideas:

* Before you start the growing, buy a bag of bean sprouts and talk about what you are going to do.
* Put the sprouted seeds in bowls for the children to look at, feel, smell, compare, talk about and finally taste.
* Try the seeds on crackers, in sandwiches, in salads mixed with grated carrot and cheese or on their own. You could try making you own Chinese food.
* Plant the seeds of flowers and vegetables and watch them grow. Collect their seeds to emphasise the growing cycle.
* Look at slower growing seeds such as carrots, and grow salad vegetables in unusual containers for example Wellington boots, old teapots.
* Keep a record of the growth of the different seeds.
* Make photographic books by taking a photo every day and adding a simple caption.
* Experiment with light and water conditions.
* Look at photos/ books, internet sites to find out about plant growth.

(check seeds used for sprouting are suitable; ask before buying, some have been sterilised and won't grow!)

Stepping Stones and Goals:

Knowledge and Understanding of the world

Yellow - Show an interest in the world in which they live

Blue - Comment and ask questions about the natural world

Green - Gain an awareness of the cultures of others

Early Learning Goals - Begin to know about their own culture and those of other people

Key Stage One Science:

Sc1 f - explore, using the senses of sight, hearing, smell, touch and taste as appropriate, and make and record observations and measurements

Sc2,3a- recognise that plants need light and water to grow

Snack type: **Soup** (a good winter snack)

Activity: **Comparing tinned, packet, fresh**

What you need: several versions of the same flavour of soup

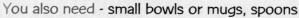

> Suggestions - tomato is a good one to try first (but you could get carrot, leek and potato etc) - shop for tinned, fresh (chilled) and packet versions
>
> You also need - small bowls or mugs, spoons

What you do:

1. Look together at the different versions of the same flavour soup. Can they tell which sort of soup it is? How does it look, and smell?
2. Let the children predict which one they think they will like best, and record their predictions. Discuss why they think soup is put in cans and packets.
3. Older children can talk about the ingredients and compare the different ingredients in the different versions. Discuss the ingredients that are good for us.
4. Now make the different sorts of soups.
5. Let the children choose which version to start with, and encourage them to compare this with the other versions. Don't give them too much to start with or they will be too full to make comparisons.
6. Talk about likes and dislikes, flavours and smells, texture and taste.
7. Record likes and dislikes over a week or several days, then try to offer a range of soups on the last day, so children can remember.
8. Use this opportunity to talk about hand washing and hygiene when cooking or preparing food.

Extensions and follow up ideas:

* Make your own soup together. Chop up some of the following: onions, carrots, tomatoes, potatoes, leeks, parsnips, swede and boil in a big saucepan till the vegetables are soft (adding a stock cube if you like). Mash the vegetables with a potato masher until the soup is smooth then reheat and eat with some crusty bread.
* Make Gazpacho or other cold soups (put 'cold soup recipes' into a search engine for free recipes on the internet).
* Collect data on favourite soups at home, get the children to ask their parents and friends at home. Invite families to a soup morning (instead of coffee).
* Put cheap root vegetables in the role play corner with suitable knives and forks (old school dining cutlery is ideal), chopping boards and pans, so children can practice cutting skills in imaginative play. Use the chopped vegetables the next day to make soup - make sure you boil it thoroughly! Teach the children to push a fork into the vegetable to hold it steady and prevent damage to fingers.
* Older children could look at packaging and design their own versions.
* Grow your own vegetables for soup: carrots, tomatoes, potatoes, leeks, peppers.

Stepping Stones and Goals:

Knowledge and Understanding of the world

Yellow - Show awareness of own needs with regard to eating and hygiene

Blue - Show awareness of a range of healthy practices

Green - Show some understanding that good practices can relate to good health

Early Learning Goals - Recognise the importance of keeping healthy and those things which contribute to this

Key Stage One Science:

Sc2 2c - that taking exercise and eating the right types and amounts of food help humans to keep healthy

Snack type: Salad

Activity: Texture and colour

What you need: a variety of salad vegetables

Suggestions - lettuce, tomatoes, cucumber, peppers, radishes, cress, celery, spring onions; salad oil, mayonnaise

You also need - bowls, small plates, safe spreading/ cutting knives, boards, colander or sieve

What you do:

1. Let the children help to wash and dry the salad vegetables.
2. Talk about each vegetable, its shape, colour and texture.
3. Cut up larger items and place each in a separate bowl so you can have a salad bar for children to choose from.
4. Encourage children to take two or three different ingredients for their individual salad and then add a little salad dressing or mayonnaise.
5. Make a chart by taking photos of each ingredient (or cutting pictures from magazines or supermarket junk mail). Children could then indicate which vegetables they have <u>tried.</u> This encourages them to 'have a go.'
6. Offer different types of the same vegetable on different occasions - different types of lettuce or leaves, different sizes of tomatoes, different colours of peppers.
7. Make a scrap book of ingredients for different salads.
8. Grow your own salad vegetables in grow-bags, pots or tubs. Children will eat almost anything they have grown themselves!

Extensions and follow up ideas:

* Make different sorts of salads - cole slaw, potato salad, beetroot, tomato and cheese etc.
* Collect salad and vegetable recipes from families and make a salad ideas book. Get parents to come and make their favourite salad with the children - take photos for the recipe book.
* Try adding some more unusual ingredients - bean sprouts, seeds, nuts, cheese cubes, tuna flakes, ham cubes, sliced courgette, hard boiled egg, herbs.
* How about adding fruit? Raisins, pineapple, cherries, strawberries, apple or pear slices, avocado, all make salad eating more interesting and tasty to young palates.
* Try preparing the same ingredient in different ways - grated or sliced carrot, chopped or sliced pepper, onion rings or chopped onion.
* Buy an Iceberg lettuce and carefully peel the leaves off, so each child can use a leaf as a plate for their salad choice.

Stepping Stones and Goals:

Knowledge and Understanding of the world

Yellow - Show curiosity

Blue - Describe simple features

Green - Examine objects and living things to find out more about them

Early Learning Goals - Investigate objects by using all of their senses as appropriate

Key Stage One Science:

Sc1 f - explore, using the senses of sight, hearing, smell, touch and taste as appropriate, and make and record observations and measurements

Organising and presenting snacks

Settings differ in the way they present snack time. Some practitioners prefer to use a more formal organisation where children all sit down together (or in key worker groups) so the time can be used for language and social development. Other practitioners prefer children to have snacks whenever they are ready, avoiding the need to stop children in the middle of an activity or when they are involved in play. You could do a mixture of both methods.

A snack bar is one way snacks and drinks can be made available when the children need them.

* For a snack bar, set aside an area with a table and chairs for snack foods and drinks that the children can access at any time. Some settings have opening times such as 8.30 - 11am and 2.00 - 4.00pm depending on the session times, others have open access all the time. It helps if the snack area is near the sink, so children can be encouraged to wash their cups and plates after snack (or put them in the dishwasher!).

* All the research tells us that children need to drink more water. Water in manageable jugs or bottles should be available at all times. Even very young children should be able to see drink jugs, so they can gesture when they are thirsty.

* When children start at the setting they will need older children or adults to model and support them in using the area appropriately.

* The area should have plates, bowls, cups and jugs with a variety of choice. It makes a good link with home to use real plates, jugs, bowls and cups rather than plastic. They are less likely to be tipped over as they are heavier and children just need to be shown what to do if one falls and breaks.

* Some settings involve interested children in preparing the snacks for 'help yourself' areas.

* Put up some photos of food and/or the children in the area to stimulate talk and remind them of how to behave during snack time.

* You could have a pictorial menu board and a till so that the children can combine role-play with snack time.

* Some settings have a rota for staff to be available in this area to promote talk and social skills. These staff may also take the children shopping for additional snack ingredients, and involve small groups in preparing or cooking the food for the day.

* An alternative to washing up in the sink is to have a bowl of soapy water and tea towels so the children can wash up after themselves.

* Some settings vary the foods according to the time of day - breakfast foods in the morning and other snacks in the afternoon.

* Some children get so involved in playing that they forget to have something to eat or drink. This is not a good idea, as small children need regular small amounts of food and drink if they are to maintain the high energy levels needed for their active learning styles. One idea for checking if children are actually getting their snack regularly is to have name cards or laminated photos for each child, so they can indicate that they have visited the café. In this way it is easy for staff to encourage and remind children who have not had a drink or snack.

Resources and web sites

Exciting projects are starting up all over the country, these include:
* 'The Kids Café' in Manchester www.use.salvationarmy.org
* 'The Cooking Bus' (a Food Standards Agency initiative available to schools across the country) www.food.gov.uk/healthiereating/bus/
* 'Food clubs' where children can have fun cooking and eating together, parents are often included in these too. If you want to start one, contact www.food.gov.uk/healthiereating/cookit
  To find out more about what is happening in your area look on your county website, search the Internet or contact your local child information service.

Books and resources in catalogues, on the Internet and in shops will enable children to explore and understand how plants grow. Here are some examples:

Books - fiction and fact
* Oliver's Vegetables/Oliver's Milkshake /Oliver's Fruit Salad; Vivien French; Hodder
* Handa's Surprise; Eileen Grown; Walker Books
* I eat Fruit/I eat Vegetables; published by Zero to Ten and available in five languages
* Eating the Alphabet/ Growing Vegetable Soup; Lois Ehlert; Harcourt
* An Alphabet Salad; S.L.Schette; Capstone Press
* Fruit/ Vegetables; Pascale De Bourgoing; Atlantic Books

Resources to look for in Early Years Catalogues:
* Root View Farm allows the children to see the roots of vegetables grow in the soil
* Miniature greenhouse, a seed growth viewer; ASCO tel: 0113 2707070
* Children's garden tools; ASCO tel: 0113 2707070
* Plastic fruit, vegetables and other foods for shopping etc; WESCO tel: 0115 986 2126

Also look for posters of foods, healthy eating games and puzzles, lotto games etc.

Useful websites

* www.bbc.co.uk/health/kids - information site for key stage one children
* www.thesnackpack.net - information, fact sheets, activities
* www.eastbourne.gov.uk/kids - links to articles, sites and activities
* www.healthvisiting.org/guides - advice sheets for parents
* http://news.bbc.co.uk/1/hi/health - information, articles and forums for parents
* www.waitrose.com/about/children - information and fact sheets
* www.bda.uk.com - food fact sheets
* www.hda-online.org.uk - recent research
* www.ivillage.co.uk/parenting - recent government research plus ideas for making fruit and vegetables more appealing to children
* www.teachernet.gov.uk/healthyliving - articles, examples of research and case studies in schools
* Bread Recipes @ www.botham.co.uk/seed/recip.htm
* Bread History @ www.botham.co.uk/bread/history1.htm
* www.nfc.u-net.com/gallery - photos of British fruit and other information
* www.google.co.uk - click on images and type in food name
* www.thefruitpages.com - information about fruit from around the world, recipes, nutritional values and fruit juice
* www.thinkvegetables.co.uk - information about vegetables, recipes, nutritional content, photos.
* www.vegsoc.org/info/cereals - basic information on cereals
* www.entertaining.about.com/od/cheeseinformation - information about cheeses.
* www.primalseeds.org/sprouting - sprouting seeds information

Some recipes

This is the way to make your own Paneer - a simple Indian recipe for cream cheese.

Ingredients

        10 cups full cream milk

        1/2 cup buttermilk or yogurt (more maybe needed, so have a bit extra)

Method

* In a large heavy bottomed pan, bring the milk to a boil over medium heat. Stir often to ensure that the milk is not sticking to the bottom of the pan.
* When milk starts to boil, lower heat and add the buttermilk and stir until the milk starts to separate into curds. If the curds are not forming, add a little more buttermilk or yogurt and cook for a couple of minutes more. And do the above as soon as the curds form.
* Remove from heat as soon as this happens. You can even add a few ice cubes to the curd-whey mix to cool it down quickly. The heat will make the protein tougher, so you need to expose the cheese to as little heat as possible.
* Pour the curds-and-whey mix into a colander lined with several layers of cheese cloth or a clean teatowel, draining onto a dish that will collect the whey.
* Collect the sides of the cheesecloth up, tie them up together and twist gently to help drain the whey from the curds.
* Place the bundled curds on a tray and press this bundle with a heavy pan/container or object. Make sure this heavy weight covers the bundle fully.
* To make a soft cheese for dessert recipes keep the weight on for half an hour.
* For a harder cheese that you can cut into cubes, weight the bundle down for an hour or more. This will make the cheese form a firm mass that can be cut into neat cubes.

Try and use the cheese the same day as you make it. The more time it is kept the dryer it becomes and the harder it will be. The cheese will get dryer if you put it in a fridge.

Maple Breakfast Bars with Dried Fruit & Nuts

You can use any type of dried fruit you like in these little oat bars. A wide variety is available in the baking section of most supermarkets, so choose your favourite, or mix and match.

Makes: 10-12.

What you need: a 20 x 25cm/8 x 10in (or similar size) tin or baking dish, a saucepan or a bowl.
* 150g/5oz butter
* 75g/3oz demerara sugar
* 75ml/3fl oz maple syrup
* 100g/3 1/2 oz dried fruit chopped into small pieces (cranberries, apricots, cherries, raisins or sultanas, dates, peaches, apples, pears etc.)
* 50g/2oz chopped toasted hazelnuts 225g/8oz rolled oats

What you do:
1. Preheat the oven to 190C/375F/gas mark 5 and grease the tin or baking dish.
2. Melt the butter in a medium saucepan.
3. Add the sugar and maple syrup and stir gently until the sugar dissolves.
4. Remove from the heat and stir in the dried fruit, nuts and oats.
5. Spread into the tin and level the top.
6. Bake for 30 minutes or until golden brown.
7. Cool slightly then mark out the bars with a knife. Allow to cool completely in the tin before removing the bars.
   (Or you can combine everything in a large bowl and heat in the microwave, stopping every 20 seconds or so to stir.)

Easy Muesli Bars

These bars are both filling and full of energy, they are perfect as snacks, eaten indoors or out.

Makes: 15

What you need:
* 1 cup rolled oats
* 3 cups crushed cornflakes
* 1 cup dessicated coconut
* 1 1/2 cups mixed dried fruit
* 3 1/2 tbsp full cream milk powder
* 4 oz butter
* 1/2 cup packed brown sugar
* 1/2 cup honey
* 1/2 cup peanut butter

What you do:
1. Mix the oats, cornflakes, coconut, dried fruit and milk powder together in a big bowl.
2. Heat butter, sugar, honey & peanut butter gently together for 3 minutes, or microwave on high for 4 minutes (from cold), stirring every minute.
3. Pour this into the dry mixture and mix well.
4. Press into a biscuit tray and put in refrigerator until cold.
5. Cut when cold.

Notes:

The bars are best kept in the refrigerator, although it's by no means essential. They soften in the heat but don't disintegrate.

Any other cereal crumbs can be combined with cornflakes to make up the 3 cups. Using Rice Krispies gives a lighter texture. Dessicated coconut is better than shredded coconut, which is too coarse.

Other titles in the Key Issues series

Boys & Girls Come Out to Play (gender)

Order **BGOP**

ISBN 1 905019 17 3

Ros Bayley and Sally Featherstone have collaborated once more to follow their successful book Smooth Transitions with this exploration of the differences in brain development, learning and behaviour between girls and boys in the Foundation Stage and Key Stage 1.

Running & Racing (fitness & health)

Order **RUN**

ISBN 1 905019 18 1

Keep on the move with this book which reflects background research and current guidance on child health and fitness. The 'heart rate raising' activities are easy to fit into your programme, need minimal equipment and are fun for everyone.

Cultures and Beliefs (a sense of identity)

Order **CAB**

ISBN 1 90501936X

Teaching in a multi-faith society presents many challenges. This book provides a detailed description of six major religions, giving a brief history of a faith and exploring the richness of its history, stories and traditions. Carefully chosen activities support your work in this area.

This important new series addresses some of the major issues facing early years settings and primary schools. The aim is to provide sound, clear advice, based on extensive knowledge and supported by the latest research. All the authors are experienced teachers and practitioners.

The series editor is Sally Featherstone.

The Key Issues strands are

- Transfer, continuity & progression
- Gender issues
- Fitness & health
- Diet & nutrition
- A sense of identity

Key Issues are available from Featherstone Education, PO Box 6390, Lutterworth LE17 6ZA.
Tel:0185 888 1212   Fax:0185 888 1360   www.featherstone.uk.com   and from selected book suppliers